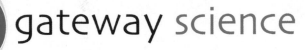
gateway science

revision guide

OCR **Science** for GCSE

Separate

Chemistry

David Lees • Roger Norris

Series editor: Bob McDuell

Heinemann

Heinemann is an imprint of Pearson Education Limited, a company incorporated in England an Wales, having its registered office at Edinburgh Gate, Harlow, Essex, CM20 2JE. Registered company number: 872828

Heinemann is a registered trademark of Pearson Education Limited

© Harcourt Education Limited 2007

First published 2007

11 10
10 9 8 7 6 5

British Library Cataloguing in Publication Data is available from the British Library on request.

ISBN: 978 0 435675 49 3

Designed by Wooden Ark
Project managed, edited and typeset by Bookcraft Ltd (Alex Sharpe, Project Manager)

Pearson project team: David Cooke, Andrew Halcro-Johnston, Ross Laman, Sarah Ross, Ruth Simms, Iti Singh, Peter Stratton

Original illustrations © Harcourt Education Limited 2007

Illustrated by Bookcraft India Pvt Ltd (Gemma Raj), HL Studios

Printed in China(EPC/05)

Cover photo © Getty Images

Every effort has been made to contact copyright holders of material reproduced in this book. Any omissions will be rectified in subsequent printings if notice is given to the publishers.

About this book

This OCR Gateway Chemistry revision guide will help you revise for the OCR Gateway Chemistry exams. One exam consists of modules C1, C2 and C3 and the other of C4, C5 and C6. The guide summarises what you have learnt and links directly to the OCR Chemistry specification for Higher tier.

This guide is broken down into the six chemistry modules: C1, C2, C3, C4, C5 and C6. Each module covers eight items (a–h), for example C1a–C1h. You will find some items are combined into one section, for example C1a & C1b.

Each section starts with a **learning outcome** which summarises the main points covered. This will help you to focus on what you need to revise in that section.

Key words are shown in bold and you will find them indexed at the back of the guide. **Equations** are highlighted to help you use and apply them.

The exam may ask you to consider ideas about 'How science works'. The **How science works** boxes will help you apply this thinking to your answers. Remember that you should be continually questioning how scientists collect data, use and interpret evidence.

Exam tips highlight common mistakes and give you advice about exam preparation so you can achieve better grades.

You will find lots of simple, full colour diagrams, including **spider diagrams**, to help with your revision and to make the content more digestible. Try drawing your own spider diagrams to help you remember key concepts.

We have given you **'Test yourself' questions** at the end of each section to help you to check that you have understood the content. Use the **answers** at the back of the guide to check whether you have got them all correct – if not, go back and revise that section again.

The revision guide is based on the new specification and the example **exam-style questions** on page 75 will give you valuable preparation for the exams.

Remember that these questions are for revision and homework. The exams will also contain some recall and one-mark questions. In your revision you should think beyond the basic ideas so that you have a better understanding for the exams.

The **answers** that follow the questions will allow you to check your progress and improve next time.

Good luck with your exams!

Contents

C1a Cooking & C1b Food additives

After revising these items you should:

- know about food cooking, additives and packaging.

Why do we cook food?

Some foods are eaten raw but most are cooked.

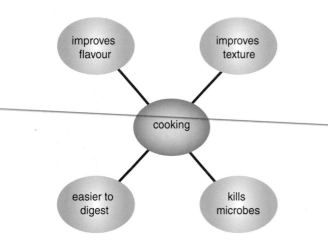

How science works

Some eggs have been found to contain bacteria called Salmonella, which can cause food poisoning.

Many people still choose to eat eggs with runny yolks. A runny yolk has not been cooked enough to kill Salmonella.

Suggest why people take this risk.

Chemical change

Cooking food is a chemical change because:

- a new substance is formed
- the change cannot be reversed (it is irreversible).

Eggs and meat are good sources of proteins. Protein molecules change shape when eggs and meat are cooked and cannot be changed back. This process is called **denaturing**. This is why egg white changes from a transparent liquid to a white solid as it is cooked.

Potatoes are a good source of **carbohydrates**. As a potato is cooked, cellulose cell walls break down releasing the cell contents. This makes the potato softer and easier to chew. It also makes it easier to digest.

Baking powder

Baking powder is added to cake mixture. The baking powder contains sodium hydrogencarbonate. When heated this breaks down, giving off the gas carbon dioxide.

$$2NaHCO_3 \longrightarrow Na_2CO_3 + H_2O + CO_2$$

sodium hydrogen carbonate $\longrightarrow$ sodium carbonate + water + carbon dioxide

The carbon dioxide gas expands in the cake mixture, making the cake rise as it is cooked.

We can show that carbon dioxide is given off in this reaction by bubbling the gas through limewater. Carbon dioxide turns limewater cloudy.

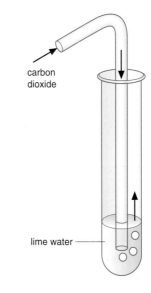

carbon dioxide

lime water

Food additives

Food additives are chemicals added to the food during processing. All approved additives are given **E-numbers**. The E-number of an additive tells us why it has been added to the food.

E-number	Type of additive	Why it is added	Some foods it is added to
E100–199	food colours	improve appearance	sweets, soft drinks, jellies
E200–299	preservatives	stop food going bad	jams, squashes
E300–399	**antioxidants**	stop reaction with oxygen	meat pies, salad cream
E400–499	**emulsifiers**	keep foods mixed	margarine, mayonnaise, salad cream
E600–699	flavourings and flavour enhancers	improve taste	sweets, meat products

How science works

Several children at a playgroup became hyperactive. All of the children at the playgroup had drunk the same brand of orange squash, which contains several food colouring additives.

These facts suggest a correlation between hyperactivity and these additives.

What additional information is needed to support the idea that these additives cause hyperactivity?

Emulsifiers

If you shake up oil and water they seem to mix. If you leave this for a few minutes the oil and water separate out again. Emulsifiers are added to food to keep the oil (or fat) and water mixed as an **emulsion**.

Emulsifiers are molecules that have a **hydrophilic** (water loving) part and a **hydrophobic** (water hating but oil or fat loving) part. The hydrophilic head of the molecule bonds to water molecules. The hydrophobic tail bonds with oil molecules. This keeps the oil and water mixed.

head   tail

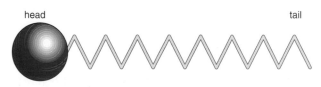

Emulsifiers turn water and oil into emulsions.

Packaging

The way that food is packaged can help to make it stay fresh for longer. Intelligent packaging can be used to improve the quality and safety of food. The material used for active packaging controls or reacts with what is taking place inside the packaging.

- If fruit is wrapped in film that has tiny holes, oxygen can enter and keep the fruit fresh for longer.
- Biscuits are wrapped in film without holes to keep out oxygen and water, so the biscuits stay crisp.
- Some foods have all of the water removed from inside the packing so that moulds cannot grow and make the food rot.
- It is possible to make cans that will heat or cool the drink inside. You can have a hot cup of coffee or an ice cold cola anywhere.

How science works

Many modern food packagings are made from plastics made from crude oil. In the past many food products were put into paper bags.

Explain one advantage for food packaging of using plastics instead of paper, and one advantage of using paper instead of plastics.

1   Why does potato taste different when it has been cooked?

2   How does the appearance of a cake show that sodium hydrogencarbonate in baking powder added to the cake mixture has decomposed as the cake cooked?

3   If meat pies are made without adding antioxidants, what may happen when they are stored for a few days?

4   Mayonnaise contains vegetable oil and vinegar. Why must it also contain an emulsifier?

5   Why do fruit and biscuits need different sorts of packaging?

C1c Smells

After revising this item you should:

●   know about the use of esters in perfumes.

Making an ester

Esters are organic compounds with characteristic sweet smells. Mixtures of different esters are used to create the distinctive smells of perfumes. An ester is made by the reaction of an alcohol with an acid.

alcohol + organic acid → ester + water

You could make an ester, with supervision from your teacher, by following these instructions.

1   Put a few cubic centimetres (cm³) of an alcohol, such as ethanol, in a test tube.

2   Add a similar volume of an organic acid, such as ethanoic acid, and stir.

3   Add one drop of concentrated sulfuric acid to act as a **catalyst** and speed up the reaction.

4   Place the test tube in a beaker of hot water for a few minutes to safely heat the mixture.

5   Pour the mixture into a beaker half filled with cold water.

Droplets of ester can be seen on the surface.

This equation shows the reaction that takes place between ethanol and ethanoic acid.

ethanol + ethanoic acid → ethyl ethanoate + water

When we show this reaction using displayed formulae it is possible to see how the two molecules join together with the loss of a water molecule.

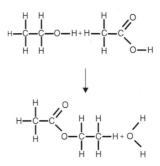

The ester ethyl ethanoate can be recognised by its sweet smell.

Esters are responsible for the sweet smell of flowers and fruit. Many of these naturally occurring esters can be manufactured in a laboratory.

Different **solvents** can be used for different jobs, because they will dissolve different **solutes**. The table below shows which solvents will dissolve wax and salt.

Solvent	Wax	Salt
ethyl ethanoate	dissolves	does not dissolve
hexane	dissolves	does not dissolve
water	does not dissolve	dissolves

Perfume properties

Each perfume has its own recognisable smell because the esters stimulate cells in the nose. To work successfully a perfume must have a number of properties.

Property of perfume	Why it is needed
evaporates easily (volatile)	so that the smelly esters can easily reach the nose
non-toxic	so that it does not poison you
does not react with water	so that it does not react with perspiration (sweat)
does not irritate the skin	so that it can be put onto the skin without causing harm
insoluble in water	so that it does not wash off easily

Volatility

The ease with which a liquid can evaporate is called its volatility. The esters in a perfume have a fairly high volatility, so that they can quickly evaporate into the air and reach the nose.

The volatility of perfumes can be explained by kinetic theory.

- During evaporation particles escape from the liquid into the air.
- Only particles with lots of energy can escape the attraction of other particles in the liquid to evaporate.
- In a perfume the attraction between the particles is weak, so the particles do not need much energy to evaporate.

This is why the esters in perfumes are volatile.

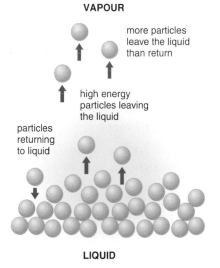

Solvents

If you have painted your nails and get fed up with the colour you will want to remove the nail varnish. It will not wash off with water, but you can remove it using nail varnish remover.

- The nail varnish is insoluble in water, but is soluble in the nail varnish remover.
- The nail varnish is a solute because it dissolves in the solvent in the nail varnish remover.
- This forms a **solution** which does not separate out.

To explain why water will not dissolve nail varnish we need to think about the attraction between particles.

- The attraction between water molecules is stronger than the attraction between water molecules and the particles in the nail varnish.
- The attraction between particles in the nail varnish is also stronger than that between water molecules and the particles in the nail varnish.
- So the attraction between water molecules and the particles in the nail varnish is not strong enough to pull the particles in the nail varnish into the water to make a solution.

Esters can be used as solvents. Ethyl ethanoate is the solvent in nail varnish remover. It has a strong enough attraction with the particles in the nail varnish to form a solution.

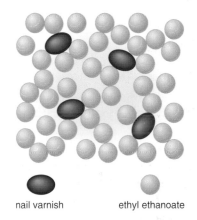

nail varnish   ethyl ethanoate

Testing cosmetics

Before a company can sell a cosmetic product to the public, the product must be tested. This is to make sure that it is safe for people to use.

The cosmetic must not be poisonous and must not cause irritation to the skin. Only when the company is certain that there are no problems is the cosmetic product marketed.

Cosmetics may be tested on animals first. The testing of cosmetics on animals is banned in the United Kingdom, but is allowed in some other countries.

Advantages of testing cosmetics on animals:

- quick   • cheap

Disadvantages of testing cosmetics on animals:

- Results on animals may not be the same as on humans.
- Many people object to animals being used for these tests.

Test yourself

1 When making esters, the mixture of different chemicals is heated in a water bath rather than using a Bunsen burner. Suggest Why.

2 Why may a company prefer to make an ester synthetically rather than extract it from a plant?

3 The esters in a perfume are dissolved in an organic solvent. This is much more volatile than the esters. Suggest why this is important.

4 Salt dissolves in water but not in ethyl ethanoate. Suggest why.

5 Some people who are against testing cosmetics on animals are not against testing medicinal drugs on animals. Suggest why.

C1d Making crude oil useful

After revising this item you should:

● know how useful products are obtained from crude oil.

Fossil fuels

Fossil fuels:

● include **crude oil**, coal and gas
● are **finite resources** of energy because one day they will run out
● are **non-renewable**.

Crude oil supplies

Large tanker ships or long pipelines are used to take the crude oil from the wells to a refinery, where it is made into useful products. Accidents can cause crude oil to be spilled, polluting land or sea and killing wildlife.

Many of the largest reserves of oil are concentrated in a few countries where there is political unrest. These countries control the output and price of the world's most important energy resource.

Developed countries such as the UK and USA are dependent on imported oil as their main source of energy. Supply restrictions and price rises can cause damage to the economies of these countries.

How science works

Transporting crude oil in tanker ships can lead to serious damage to the environment if there is an accident. Despite this possibility, millions of tons of crude oil are transported across the seas each year.

Suggest why oil is transported in this way.

Fractional distillation

Crude oil contains **hydrocarbon** molecules of different sizes, ranging from those with just one carbon atom to those with over 50 carbon atoms. The displayed formulae of four of these hydrocarbon molecules are shown below.

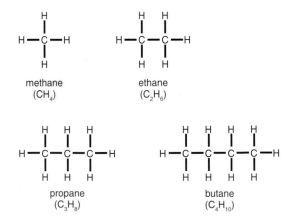

methane
(CH_4)

ethane
(C_2H_6)

propane
(C_3H_8)

butane
(C_4H_{10})

To make useful products from crude oil it is separated into **fractions** using a **fractional distillation** column.

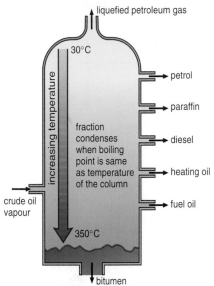

liquefied petroleum gas

30°C

increasing temperature

petrol

paraffin

fraction condenses when boiling point is same as temperature of the column

diesel

heating oil

crude oil vapour

fuel oil

350°C

bitumen

In hydrocarbon molecules the hydrogen and carbon atoms are held together by very strong **covalent** bonds. These do not break when the hydrocarbon boils.

The **intermolecular** forces between hydrocarbon molecules are much weaker. When the hydrocarbon boils these break, releasing the molecules as a vapour.

The intermolecular forces between large hydrocarbon molecules are stronger than those between small hydrocarbon molecules. So the larger the hydrocarbon molecules the more energy is needed to separate them, and therefore the higher the **boiling point**.

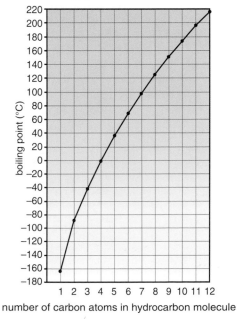

boiling point (°C)

number of carbon atoms in hydrocarbon molecule

Fractional distillation works like this:

- The fractionating column is hottest at the bottom and coldest at the top.
- As crude oil vapour passes up the column it cools and each hydrocarbon condenses when it reaches its boiling point.
- This means that hydrocarbon molecules of different sizes condense at different heights up the column.
- Each fraction, containing several hydrocarbons with similar boiling points, is collected to make a different product.
- The nearer the top of the column the fraction is collected, the lower the boiling points and the smaller the molecules of the hydrocarbons it contains.

Supply and demand

We use a lot of some of the fractions, but less of others. From crude oil we get more of some of the less useful fractions and less of some of the more useful ones.

> **Exam tip**
>
> *You do not need to learn details of supply and demand for the fractions, but in an exam you may be given this information and asked questions about it.*

Cracking

A process called **cracking** is used to get more of the fractions we use most. This is carried out at a high temperature, using a catalyst to speed up the reaction.

Most of the hydrocarbons in crude oil belong to a chemical family called **alkanes**. Cracking breaks some of the larger, less useful alkanes to make more of the smaller and more useful ones. This equation shows the cracking of the large alkane decane.

$$C_{10}H_{22} \longrightarrow C_8H_{18} + C_2H_4$$
decane   octane   ethene

Petrol contains octane and other hydrocarbons of similar size, so cracking produces more of the petrol fraction.

In the cracking reaction hydrocarbons belonging to another chemical family, the **alkenes**, are also formed.

These are very useful substances, and are used to make **polymers**. Ethene is used to make poly(ethene), the most widely used polymer.

C1e Making polymers & C1f Designer polymers

After revising these items you should:

- know how polymers are made and used.

Making polymers

Plastics are made of polymers, which are very large molecules. Polymer molecules are made by joining together lots of small molecules, called **monomers**.

The reaction used to make a polymer from a monomer is called polymerisation, and is carried out at high pressure using a catalyst.

Many polymers are made from alkenes. These are called addition polymers because the monomer molecules add together to make the polymer without forming any other product. During **addition polymerisation** many small **unsaturated** molecules join to form each large **saturated** polymer molecule.

Poly(ethene) is the polymer made by joining together lots of ethene molecules. This polymer is commonly called polythene.

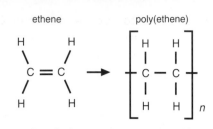

The polymerisation of ethene.

Exam tip

You need to know the formula of methane and ethane.

Alkanes

Crude oil is a mixture of hydrocarbons, which are molecules containing the elements hydrogen and carbon only. Most of the hydrocarbons in crude oil belong to a family called the alkanes. The diagram shows displayed formulae of the first three alkanes.

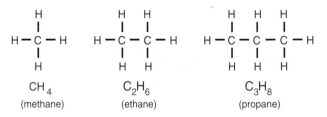

CH_4 (methane) C_2H_6 (ethane) C_3H_8 (propane)

In these molecules hydrogen atoms and carbon atoms share a pair of **electrons** to form a covalent bond. The alkanes are said to be saturated because they contain single covalent bonds only.

Alkenes

The alkenes are another family of hydrocarbons. Alkenes are said to be unsaturated because they have one or more double covalent bonds between carbon atoms. The diagram shows the displayed formulae of two alkenes.

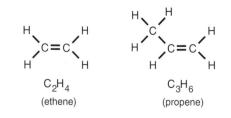

C_2H_4 (ethene) C_3H_6 (propene)

Bromine can be used to test if a compound is saturated or unsaturated.

- When an unsaturated compound such as ethene is bubbled through orange-red bromine water the colour disappears.
- With a saturated compound such as ethane there is no colour change.

The reaction that takes place with ethene is shown in the diagram below.

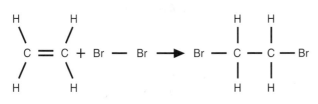

The reaction between ethene and bromine.

Designer polymers

Different polymers have different properties. We use a polymer for a particular job because it has the right properties.

The atoms in the polymer chains of plastics are held together by strong covalent bonds. Some plastics have weak intermolecular forces between polymer molecules, so they have low melting points and can be stretched easily.

An example is poly(ethene), which is good for making articles such as plastic bags, buckets and washing up bowls.

Other plastics have strong forces between the polymer molecules. These may be covalent **crosslinking** bridges between adjacent polymer molecules.

These polymers have high melting points, cannot be stretched and are rigid. They are good for making articles that have to withstand high temperatures, such as kettles.

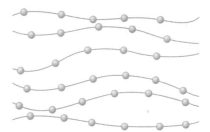

Particles in poly(ethene).

This polymer has links between the polymer chains.

Clothing

Outdoor coats may be made of nylon or Gore-Tex®. Nylon is tough, lightweight, waterproof and keeps out UV light. But it does not let water vapour out, so sweat condenses inside the coat. Gore-Tex® is made from nylon laminated with a PTFE/polyurethane membrane.

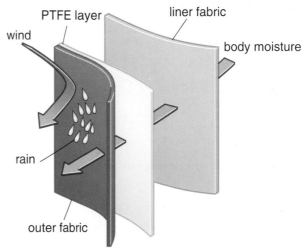

The structure of Gore-Tex®.

Holes in the PTFE layer are too small to let water pass through, so rain water cannot get through the coat. The holes are big enough to let water vapour pass through, so sweat can escape as water vapour. This makes the coat waterproof but breathable.

Disposal of polymers

Many polymers, such as poly(ethene), are non-biodegradable. This means that:

- they will not be decomposed or decayed by the action of bacteria
- if they are carelessly thrown away they cause litter
- they can be disposed of in landfill sites, but landfill sites get filled quickly and waste valuable land
- they can be disposed of by burning, but this produces toxic gases.

Both landfill and burning mean that a valuable resource has been wasted.

It is also possible to **recycle** non-biodegradable polymers:

- when a polymer is recycled it can be used again
- but different polymers have to be separately sorted out of the waste, which makes recycling difficult and expensive.

In the future it is likely that many new **biodegradable** polymers will be made.

C1g Using carbon fuels

Choosing the right fuel

We burn fossil fuels to get energy. The amount of fossil fuels we use is increasing as the demand for energy for industry, transport and heating homes increases. Which fuel we use for a particular job depends on a number of factors. The table shows these factors for four fossil fuels.

Complete combustion

A fuel is a substance that reacts with oxygen to release useful energy. This is the process of burning, or **combustion**.

Complete combustion of a hydrocarbon fuel (e.g. petrol):

• requires a plentiful supply of air or oxygen

• releases the maximum amount of energy

• makes only carbon dioxide and water.

We can carry out a simple laboratory demonstration to show that natural gas (methane) is a hydrocarbon fuel.

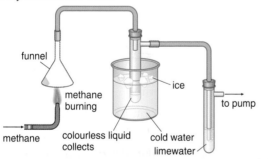

A colourless liquid collects in the tube cooled by the ice. This liquid is water. The limewater goes cloudy, showing that carbon dioxide has been made. The complete combustion of methane is shown by this equation.

$$CH_4 + 2O_2 \longrightarrow CO_2 + 2H_2O$$
$$\text{methane} + \text{oxygen} \longrightarrow \text{carbon dioxide} + \text{water}$$

How science works

A number of years ago, some scientists predicted that carbon dioxide produced by burning fossil fuels would increase the greenhouse effect and so lead to global warming.

Since then measurements have shown that the average annual temperature in many places on the Earth's surface has increased.

What does this suggest about the confidence that we can have in the predictions made by these scientists?

Incomplete combustion

When there is not enough oxygen for a fuel to burn completely, **incomplete combustion** takes place.

Incomplete combustion happens if the fuel does not get a good enough air supply. It gives a cooler yellow flame. This flame contains a lot of soot, which is unburned carbon from the fuel. Carbon monoxide is also produced.

$$4CH_4 + 5O_2 \longrightarrow 2CO + 2C + 8H_2O$$
$$\text{methane} + \text{oxygen} \longrightarrow \text{carbon monoxide} + \text{carbon} + \text{water}$$

Fuel	Relative cost	Energy value	Availability	Storage	Toxicity	Pollution	Ease of use
coal	cheap	medium	available	easy to store	non-toxic	smoky	difficult to catch alight
oil	expensive	high	widely available	has to be stored in a tank	leaking gas can be poisonous	little pollution	easy to burn
gas from gas main	moderate	high	only in places where there is a gas main	supply directly to house	gas non-toxic; leaks can cause explosion	little pollution	easy to burn
gas in cylinders	expensive	high	widely available	in heavy cylinders	gas non-toxic; leaks can cause explosion	little pollution	easy to burn

When a Bunsen burner air hole is opened complete combustion takes place, giving a hotter blue flame. The blue flame produces more energy than the yellow flame. The blue flame does not produce soot.

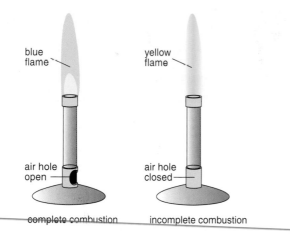

complete combustion   incomplete combustion

Test yourself

1 Look at the table on page 11. Which is the best fuel to use in a house in a rural village which does not have a gas main? Explain your choice.

2 Why is the tube that collects liquid water in a complete combustion experiment placed in a beaker of iced water?

3 Propane, C_3H_8, is sold in red cylinders. Write symbol and word equations for the complete combustion of propane.

4 Butane, C_4H_{10}, is sold in blue cylinders. Construct an equation for the incomplete combustion of butane.

5 Why does a blue Bunsen burner flame produce more energy than a yellow Bunsen burner flame?

6 Why might it be dangerous to use a gas fire that has not been serviced for a long time?

Exam tip

Make sure that you can construct symbol equations for the complete and incomplete combustion of the common fuel gases methane, propane and butane given the formula of the fuel.

Servicing gas fires

When servicing a gas fire or boiler the engineer makes sure that the burning gas has a good supply of air so that complete combustion takes place. In a poor supply of air incomplete combustion takes place. This causes three problems:

• The fire gives out less heat.

• Soot is produced.

• The poisonous gas carbon monoxide is made.

How science works

There are clear advantages in having gas fires and boilers serviced. There are risks involved in not having gas appliances serviced.

Despite this, many people choose not to have their gas appliances serviced. Suggest why.

C1h Energy

After revising this item you should:

● know about reactions that give out or take in energy.

Exothermic or endothermic

When a piece of magnesium ribbon is dropped into a test tube containing dilute hydrochloric acid:

• a chemical reaction takes place

• the acid bubbles as hydrogen is given off

• the test tube gets hotter

• a thermometer placed in the acid will show an increase in temperature.

The reaction between magnesium and hydrochloric acid is an **exothermic** reaction. During the reaction energy is released.

Some chemical reactions take energy in from the surroundings. If you add solid sodium hydrogencarbonate to a solution of citric acid in a test tube:

• a chemical reaction takes place

• bubbles of carbon dioxide are seen

• the tube feels cold

• a thermometer placed in the mixture will show a decrease in temperature.

The reaction between sodium hydrogencarbonate and citric acid is an **endothermic** reaction. During the reaction energy is taken in.

Bond breaking and bond making

During a chemical reaction, bonds in the **reactants** are broken and new bonds are made in the products.

Energy is needed to break bonds and energy is given out when bonds are formed.

Whether a reaction is exothermic or endothermic depends on the difference between the energy needed to break the bonds of the reactants and the energy given out as the bonds in the **products** are formed.

When methane burns, the bonds in each methane molecule and oxygen molecule are broken.

$$CH_4 \ + \ 2O_2 \ \longrightarrow \ CO_2 \ + \ 2H_2O$$

During the reaction the bonds in each carbon dioxide molecule and water molecule are formed.

Bonds broken: 4 C–H and 2 O=O

Bonds formed: 2 C=O and 4 O–H

In this reaction more energy is released from forming bonds than the energy absorbed from breaking bonds. This excess energy is released as heat into the surroundings. The reaction is exothermic.

Measuring energy changes

The diagram shows a method that can be used to compare the energy transferred in different combustion reactions.

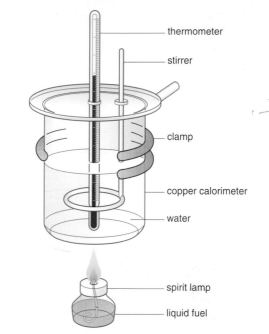

- thermometer
- stirrer
- clamp
- copper calorimeter
- water
- spirit lamp
- liquid fuel

- A measured volume of water is placed in a copper container called a **calorimeter**.
- The water is heated by the combustion of a liquid fuel in a spirit lamp.
- A stirrer is used to make sure that all of the water is at the same temperature.
- A thermometer is used to measure the temperature before and after the liquid fuel is burned.
- The bottle of liquid fuel is weighed before and after the experiment to find how much of the liquid has been burned.

We can use the information from this experiment to calculate the amount of heat released when different liquid fuels are burned. To make this a fair test, the same amount of water is used for each liquid fuel. The heat released is calculated, in joules (J), for the combustion of the same mass of liquid fuel.

The table shows results for an experiment using ethanol in the spirit lamp.

mass of water used	100 g
temperature of water at the start	18°C
temperature of water at the end	32°C
mass of spirit lamp at the start	98.42 g
mass of spirit lamp at the end	96.32 g

The amount of heat energy transferred to the water can be calculated using this formula:

$$\text{energy (J)} = \frac{\text{mass of}}{\text{water (g)}} \times \frac{\text{temperature}}{\text{rise (°C)}} \times 4.2$$

This gives the energy in joules (J), so the answer must be divided by 1000 to be in kilojoules (kJ). This figure is then divided by the mass of fuel burned (in grams) to get the energy output per gram of fuel.

Exam tip

It is a good idea to practise this sort of calculation. In an exam question you may be given experimental data and asked to work out the energy output of a fuel.

How science works

The energy output calculated from this data is less than the actual energy given out when 1.0 g of ethanol is burned. Suggest why the design of this experiment does not give a more accurate result.

Test yourself

1 When magnesium ribbon is added to dilute hydrochloric acid, what do you see that tells you a chemical reaction is taking place?

2 The reaction between sodium hydrogencarbonate and citric acid is endothermic. What does this tell you about the bonds in the reactants and products in this reaction?

3 Why is it important to stir the water in the calorimeter while the fuel is burning?

4 When experiments are carried out using several different liquid fuels, a different mass of each fuel is burned. But the heat released by each fuel is calculated per g of fuel burned. Why is the heat released calculated in this way?

5 Use the information in the table of results for the experiment using ethanol in the spirit lamp to work out the energy output per gram of ethanol.

6 Similar apparatus can be used to measure the heat released when gaseous or solid fuels are burned. The table below shows a comparison of the heat released by the combustion of some fuels.

Fuel	State of fuel	Energy produced (kJ/g)
hydrogen	gas	243
methane	gas	56
ethanol	liquid	30
petrol	liquid	48

Methane gives out more energy for each 1 g burned than petrol, but most cars are fuelled by petrol rather than methane. Suggest a reason for this.

C2a Paints and pigments & C2b Construction materials

Paint ingredients

Paints contain several substances, including a pigment, a solvent and a binding medium. These ingredients are mixed together to form a **colloid**. This is a mixture where solid particles are mixed and dispersed with particles of a liquid, but are not dissolved in the liquid. In paint the solid pigment and binding medium particles are dispersed throughout the liquid solvent particles.

The components of a colloid will not separate because the particles are scattered or dispersed throughout the mixture and are so small that they will not settle out at the bottom.

Paint is applied as a thin layer and the solvent evaporates as the paint dries. Some paints are oil-based, with a hydrocarbon solvent that evaporates quickly. As they dry the oil is oxidised by oxygen in the air to form a hard, durable finish.

Other paints are water-based. They are often called emulsion paints because they are made of a colloid called an emulsion. This contains the pigment and binding agent dispersed through water.

The table shows some properties and uses of these paints.

Paint	Finish	Cleaning of brushes	Uses
oil-based	high gloss	a solvent must be used	indoor and outdoor woodwork
emulsion	matt or satin	can be cleaned in water	indoor walls

Exam tip

A colloid is a mixture of two substances that do not normally mix. There are many examples, such as milk, butter, mayonnaise, smoke.

Dyes

Dyes are used to colour fabrics.

- Some dyes are natural. Most natural dyes are obtained from plants. This means that there is only a limited range of colours available.
- Other dyes are synthetic. These are made in factories. The use of synthetic dyes has increased the number of colours available to colour fabrics.

How science works

The raw materials used to make synthetic dyes are obtained from crude oil. Explain why using natural dyes is more sustainable than using synthetic dyes.

Pigments with special properties

Thermochromic pigments change colour when heated or cooled. They can be used on the outside of electric kettles to show how hot the water is. They can also be used to warn that the liquid in a cup is hot. Thermochromic pigments can be added to acrylic paints to give even more colour changes.

Phosphorescent pigments can glow in the dark. They absorb and store energy and release it as light over a period of time. They can be used to make paints glow in the dark. Paints containing phosphorescent pigments are used to make watch faces that can be seen in the dark. They are much safer than the radioactive substances that were once used for this purpose.

Construction materials

Many **construction materials** are used to build houses and other buildings. Some of these construction materials are made from rocks in the Earth's **crust**. Examples are shown in the table.

Construction material	Source
aluminium	aluminium **ore**
iron	iron ore
brick	clay
cement and **concrete**	limestone, clay, sand, gravel
glass	sand

We can also use rocks themselves as construction materials. Buildings can be made from blocks of:

- **granite**
- **limestone**
- **marble**

Granite is an **igneous** rock. It is the hardest of these three materials, and will withstand weathering and the wear and tear of daily use.

Limestone and marble are both made of calcium carbonate, but marble is much harder than limestone. Limestone is a sedimentary rock. Marble is a metamorphic rock made by the action of high pressures and high temperatures on limestone. The hardness of a rock depends on how it was formed.

Using limestone

Thermal decomposition is a reaction in which one substance is chemically changed by heating into at least two new substances. When heated strongly, limestone thermally decomposes to make calcium oxide and carbon dioxide.

$$CaCO_3 \longrightarrow CaO + CO_2$$

calcium carbonate $\longrightarrow$ calcium oxide + carbon dioxide

> **Exam tip**
>
> *You should learn the definition of thermal decomposition.*

When limestone is heated together with clay, cement is made. We can mix it with sand or gravel and water and the mixture sets to form concrete.

Concrete is very hard but to make it stronger the concrete is set around steel supports to make reinforced concrete. It is a **composite** material because it contains more than one material put together to make a new material.

Reinforced concrete has the hardness of concrete together with the flexibility and strength of steel. This makes it a better construction material than non-reinforced concrete.

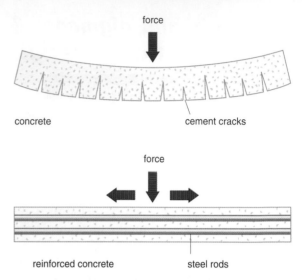

Steel rods make concrete stronger.

> **Test yourself**
>
> 1 Suggest why outdoor woodwork is painted with oil-based paint rather than emulsion paint.
>
> 2 Why do synthetic dyes have more colours than natural dyes?
>
> 3 Suggest why phosphorescent paints are safer for watch faces than paints containing radioactive substances.
>
> 4 Suggest why marble is harder than limestone.
>
> 5 Many tall buildings are made using reinforced concrete. What might happen if steel supports were not put into the concrete?

C2c Does the Earth move?

> **After revising this item you should:**
>
> - know how plate tectonics is changing the appearance of the Earth.

Structure of the Earth

The Earth is a sphere with a thin solid rocky crust, semi-liquid **mantle** and a **core** containing mainly iron. The outer layer of the Earth is cold and rigid, and is called the **lithosphere**. This includes the crust and the outer part of the mantle.

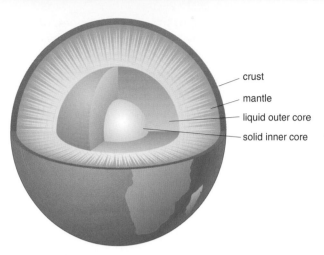

crust
mantle
liquid outer core
solid inner core

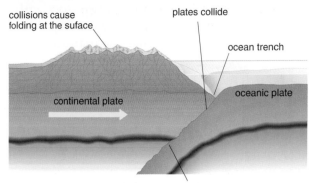

collisions cause folding at the suface
plates collide
ocean trench
continental plate
oceanic plate
rock forced down into mantle

The mantle is the zone between the crust and the core. Deep below the crust the mantle is hot and non-rigid. Here the molten rock, called **magma**, can flow. Just below the core the mantle is cooler and rigid.

The crust is 'cracked' into huge pieces called **tectonic plates**. Oceanic plates lie beneath the oceans and continental plates form the continents. The tectonic plates are less dense than the mantle and float on top of it.

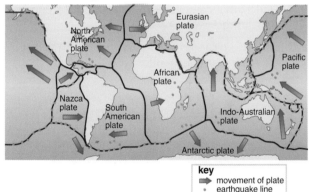

North American plate
Eurasian plate
Pacific plate
African plate
Nazca plate
South American plate
Indo-Australian plate
Antarctic plate

key
movement of plate
earthquake line

Convection currents in the mantle transfer energy to the plates, causing them to move very slowly. In places the oceanic and continental plates collide. Because oceanic plates are more dense than continental plates, as they collide the oceanic plate slides beneath the continental plate. This is called **subduction**, and may result in the partial remelting of tectonic plates.

Volcanoes and igneous rocks

Molten rock, called magma, from the mantle can find its way up through weaknesses in the Earth's crust. Since this magma rises through the crust it shows that the magma is less dense than the crust.

In a **volcano** the magma is forced out onto the surface of the Earth as a stream of **lava**.

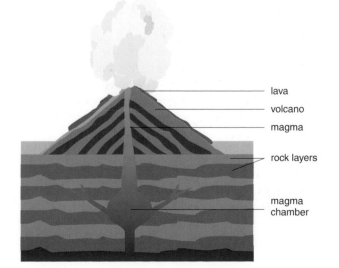

lava
volcano
magma
rock layers
magma chamber

The lava cools quickly to form igneous rock with small crystals. The type of rock formed depends on the composition of the magma that was forced to the surface.

- Iron-rich magma, which is runny and gives lava that runs slowly from the volcano, forms **basalt**.
- Silica-rich magma, which gives lava that is ejected explosively, forms **rhyolite**.

Explosive eruptions may eject pumice and volcanic ash and bombs, sometimes with graded bedding.

When magma is forced up through cracks in the crust but does not reach as far as the surface, it cools more slowly. This forms igneous rocks with large crystals, such as gabbro and granite.

Exam tip

You need to know how the size of crystals in igneous rocks is related to the rate at which the magma cooled when the rocks were formed.

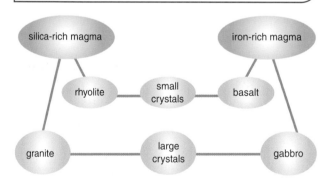

Studying the structure

Studying the structure of the Earth is not easy. Most of our knowledge of the mantle and core has been gained by using instruments. We cannot drill far enough down into the Earth to reach deeper than the upper part of the crust.

We can see magma when it is ejected from volcanoes, though it is hazardous to get near enough to investigate. Geologists study volcanoes to reveal information about the structure of the Earth, but also to enable them to predict future eruptions.

Many people choose to live near volcanoes, often because the soil there is very fertile. They need to be warned if an eruption is about to take place.

How science works

Geologists would like to be able to predict exactly where and when volcanic eruptions and earthquakes will occur, so they study and take measurements of volcanoes and plate movements.

Their predictions are now much better than they were thirty years ago, but they still cannot predict with 100 per cent certainty.

Suggest why.

Test yourself

1 Why may subduction result in the partial remelting of tectonic plates?

2 Volcanoes that eject iron-rich lava are said to be 'safer' than those that eject silica-rich lava. Suggest why.

3 The rocks around a volcano have small crystals. Explain why.

4 Under what conditions does magma cool to form igneous rock with large crystals?

5 How do volcanoes show us that the Earth's crust is denser than the mantle?

C2d Metals and alloys

After revising this item you should:

- know the properties and uses of some metals and alloys.

Copper

The copper extracted from copper ores is pure enough for some uses, such as water pipes. It is not pure enough for making electrical wiring, since impurities increase resistance in the wire.

Impure copper is purified using **electrolysis**. The diagram on the next page shows apparatus for a laboratory demonstration to show this.

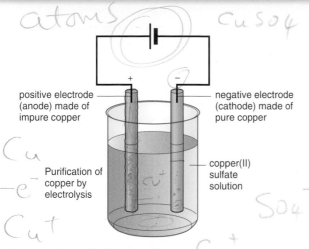

Copper can be purified by electrolysis.

The positive **electrode** (**anode**) is made of impure copper. During electrolysis copper leaves this electrode and is deposited on the negative electrode (**cathode**) which is made of pure copper. The **electrolyte** is copper(II) sulfate solution. Impurities dissolve in this solution or fall to the bottom of the cell.

Exam tip

You need to remember which electrode is impure copper and which is pure copper. As an aid to remembering this you could say 'I am positive that the copper is not pure', showing that the positive electrode is made of impure copper.

Recycling copper

Copper is a fairly expensive metal. It is much cheaper to collect and recycle copper that has already been used than to make new copper.

It also saves resources. The Earth has a finite amount of copper ore, and we use a large amount each year. One day we may run out.

There are, however, some problems involved in recycling copper. For example:

- It requires a lot of organisation. Places have to be set up for the used copper to be collected and stored, and people need to be told where these are.
- Most people do not realise the advantage of recycling copper, and simply throw it away. They need to be encouraged to recycle it.

How science works

Explain the advantages of recycling copper instead of extracting it from copper ore.

Alloys

An **alloy** is a mixture of two elements, at least one of which is a metal. Many alloys contain two or more metals mixed together. Examples of alloys are brass, bronze, solder, steel and amalgam. More details about some of these alloys are shown in the table.

Alloy	Main metal	Use
amalgam	mercury	tooth fillings
brass	copper and zinc	hinges, screws, ornaments
solder	lead and tin	joining wires and water pipes

Exam tip

You need to know which metals are in each of these three alloys.

Alloy properties

Alloys have properties that are different from those of the metals that they contain. These may make the alloy more useful than the pure metal.

Copper is a fairly soft metal, and reacts with air to form a green coating. Brass is much harder than copper, and is resistant to **corrosion**. This property makes brass more suitable for making hinges and screws than copper.

The table gives details of some properties of the alloy solder, and the metals tin and lead that are mixed together to make it.

Metal	solder	tin	lead
Melting point (°C)	110–130	232	328
Density (g/cm³)	10.3	9.3	11.3
Relative hardness	quite hard	soft	soft

Solder is used to make connections between components in electrical equipment such as radios and computers. Some of these components are damaged at high temperatures.

Smart alloys

Nitinol is an alloy made from nickel and titanium. It has the unusual property of retaining its shape. If you accidentally sit on a pair of spectacles with nitinol frames, they simply spring back into shape.

These **smart alloys** also have military and medical uses. Smart alloys can be used to hold badly fractured bones in place while they heal.

Test yourself

1 The total mass of the apparatus used to purify copper does not change during electrolysis. Suggest why.

2 Copper(II) sulfate solution is blue. Its colour does not change when it is used as an electrolyte during the purification of copper. Explain why.

3 Suggest why only a small proportion of the copper we use is recycled.

4 Steel is a mixture of iron and carbon. How is this mixture different from those in the table of alloys?

5 Suggest why solder is better than lead for making electrical connections in a computer.

C2e Cars for scrap

After revising this item you should:

● know about the metals and alloys used in cars.

Rusting

Iron in contact with water and oxygen forms **rust**. Rusting is an oxidation reaction where iron reacts with water and oxygen to form hydrated iron(III) oxide.

iron + oxygen + water ⟶ hydrated iron(III) oxide

How fast iron rusts depends on the conditions it is in. Salt water and acid rain both speed up the rate of iron rusting.

Iron is the only metal that rusts. Some other metals corrode when exposed to water and oxygen, but aluminium does not. The surface of aluminium has a thin coating of aluminium oxide that protects the metal beneath it from corrosion.

Exam tip

In an exam question you may be given information about the rates of corrosion of different metals in different conditions. You may be asked to interpret this data.

Steel

Steel is an alloy of iron. An alloy is a mixture of two elements, one of which is a metal. Many alloys contain two or more metals mixed together, but to make steel iron is mixed with a very small percentage of carbon, a non-metal.

Like many other alloys, the properties of steel are quite different from those of the metal it is made from.

● Steel is harder than iron.
● Steel is stronger than iron.
● Steel is less likely to corrode than iron.

These properties make steel more useful than iron.

How science works

Scientists tested the hardness of several samples from the same batch of steel. They found that one hardness value was far lower than the others.

Suggest what may have caused this.

Aluminium cars

We can make a car body from aluminium instead of steel. Aluminium has a number of advantages over steel for this use, for example:

● an aluminium car body is lighter than one made of steel, giving better fuel economy
● an aluminium car body will corrode less than a steel body and so may have a longer lifetime.

Aluminium does, however, have one disadvantage:

● A similar car body will be more expensive when made of aluminium rather than steel.

Materials used to make cars

Many materials are used to make a car. We can see this from the pie chart.

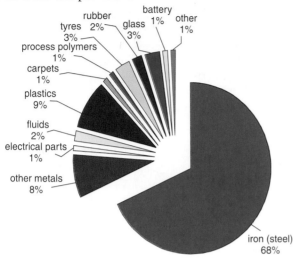

Materials used in cars.

Each part of the car is made from a material that has properties that make it suitable for use in that part of the car. For example:

- the body is made of steel because it is strong and can be shaped easily
- seat coverings are made of fibres because they are flexible, durable and can be dyed to give attractive colours
- tyres are made of rubber because it is flexible and hardwearing, but it is strengthened by fibres or steel mesh
- the windscreen is made of glass because it is transparent and scratch resistant.

Recycling metals

We are able to recycle many materials, including some of those used to make cars. There are advantages and problems associated with recycling, as shown in the spider diagram below.

In the United Kingdom it is likely that new laws about materials in cars will soon be passed. These will make sure that a minimum percentage of the materials used to make new cars is recyclable.

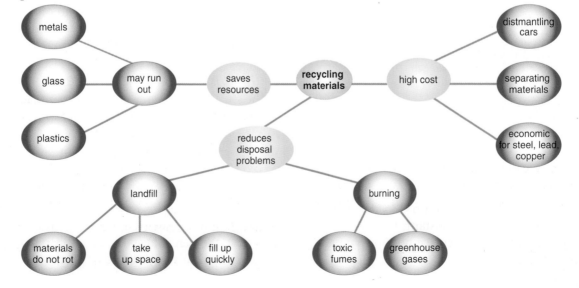

1 If you live near the sea your car is likely to rust faster than if you lived inland. Suggest why.

2 An aluminium body is more likely to be found on a sports car than on a family hatchback. Explain why.

3 Which material is most of a car made from? Why?

4 More steel is recycled from cars than any other material. Suggest why.

5 Suggest why copper wiring is stripped from cars and the copper recycled, but PVC on the dashboard and inside the doors is not.

C2f Clean air

After revising this item you should:

● know about the composition of clean air and the gases that pollute it.

Gases in the air

The pie chart shows the composition by volume of clean, dry air. Air also contains a variable amount of water vapour.

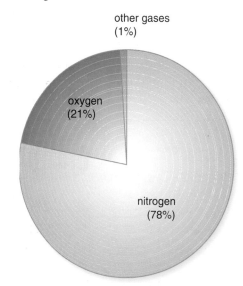

other gases (1%)

oxygen (21%)

nitrogen (78%)

Of the 'other gases', 0.35 per cent is carbon dioxide.

The oxygen, nitrogen and carbon dioxide levels in the air are approximately constant. Processes in the carbon cycle remove and replace both oxygen and carbon dioxide.

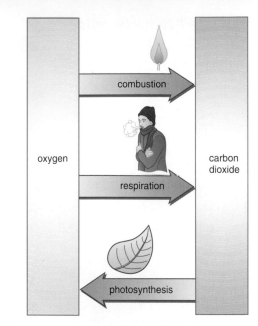

combustion

oxygen

respiration

carbon dioxide

photosynthesis

Keeping oxygen and carbon dioxide in balance.

During **photosynthesis** plants remove carbon dioxide from the air and release oxygen into the air. During **respiration** in plants and animals, and during combustion, oxygen is removed from the air and carbon dioxide is released into the air.

In the carbon cycle these processes balance out, so that the proportion of these two gases in the air does not change.

However, the activities of an increasing population of humans have caused changes in the composition of the air, for example:

● **deforestation** is reducing the amount of carbon dioxide removed by trees

● increased burning of fossil fuels to obtain energy is releasing more carbon dioxide into the air.

Evolution of the atmosphere

The Earth's atmosphere was not always as it is today. The original atmosphere came from gases escaping from the interior of the Earth. This atmosphere contained a lot of carbon dioxide, but no oxygen.

When plants evolved they carried out the process of photosynthesis. This removed carbon dioxide from the air and released oxygen into the air. Gradually the percentage of oxygen in the air increased until it reached today's level.

A theory to explain the evolution of our atmosphere involves several ideas:

1 degassing from the Earth's crust (as gases such as carbon dioxide, steam, ammonia and methane were released from volcanoes)

2 this formed an initial atmosphere of ammonia and carbon dioxide

3 formation of liquid water from steam as the Earth cooled

4 development of photosynthetic organisms that used up carbon dioxide and produced oxygen

5 conversion of ammonia into nitrogen by the action of bacteria

6 this leads to an increase in oxygen and nitrogen levels

7 lack of reactivity of nitrogen resulting in nitrogen remains as the main atmospheric gas due to its lack of reactivity.

Exam tip

You may be asked to describe a theory of how the Earth's atmosphere evolved.

Air pollution

Human activities have released other gases into the air, causing **atmospheric pollution**. The most important of these pollutant gases are shown in the table.

Pollutant	How it forms	Effects
carbon monoxide	incomplete combustion of petrol or diesel in car engines	poisonous gas
oxides of nitrogen	in car engines from the reaction of nitrogen and oxygen	**acid rain** and photochemical smog
sulfur dioxide	combustion of fossil fuels containing sulfur, for example, coal	acid rain

Exam tip

You may be given information about the effects of atmospheric pollutants and asked to interpret this.

How science works

The table shows measurements of sulfur dioxide made at the side of a busy road. The measurements were made at the same time of day for five consecutive days. Similar measurements were made at the side of a quiet country road.

Sulfur dioxide concentration ($\mu g/m^3$)					
day	1	2	3	4	5
busy road	81	79	82	80	78
country road	12	10	14	11	13

Obtain a best estimate of the sulfur dioxide **concentration** at each location by working out the mean (average) of each set of five results.

Scientists conclude from these results that sulfur dioxide is being released in car exhaust fumes. How do the results give confidence in this conclusion?

Exam tip

You may be asked to make similar calculations in an exam question.

Reducing air pollution

Pollutant gases are harmful. Acid rain can corrode metals, damage buildings and harm plants and aquatic life. Smog can cause breathing difficulties in humans. It is therefore important that atmospheric pollution is controlled.

The carbon monoxide given out by car engines is very poisonous. By law, all new cars made in the United Kingdom have to be fitted with a catalytic converter. This removes carbon monoxide from the exhaust gases of the car. The catalytic converter changes carbon monoxide into carbon dioxide.

$$2CO + 2NO \longrightarrow N_2 + 2CO_2$$

Scientists examined the health of people living near an iron foundry. The company which operates the foundry introduced a programme to reduce air pollution.

The scientists compared figures for hospital asthma admissions for two years before the improvements were made and for two years after.

They found that the number of patients admitted to hospital with asthma fell by 30 per cent after the foundry reduced emissions of pollutants.

This research shows a correlation between air pollution and asthma.

Explain why this data does not prove that asthma is caused by air pollution.

What further information would support the idea that air pollution causes asthma?

What else could have been responsible for the observed data?

Test yourself

1 Why is the composition of the air given for dry air?

2 Suggest why an increasing human population has an effect on the composition of the air.

3 Suggest why the lack of reactivity of nitrogen is important in the evolution of our atmosphere.

4 Look at the table of pollutant gases. What is similar about the way they are formed?

5 Many scientists believe that an increase in carbon dioxide in the air increases the greenhouse effect and leads to global warming. State and explain the effect that catalytic converters will have on the level of carbon dioxide in the air.

C2g Faster or slower? (1) & C2h Faster or slower? (2)

After revising these items you should:

● know what makes reactions take place at different rates.

Reaction rate

The **rate of a chemical reaction** depends on two things:

● The frequency at which reacting particles collide.

● The energy transferred during the collision.

Increasing reaction rates

The rate of a reaction can be increased by increasing the temperature. At a higher temperature the particles move faster and have more energy, so:

● there are more collisions per second

● each collision has more energy

● the proportion of successful collisions is greater.

This makes the reaction faster.

More collisions as the temperature rises.

The rate of a reaction can be increased by increasing the concentration of one of the reactants, because:

● at a higher concentration the particles are more crowded

● the particles collide more often.

This makes the reaction faster.

If the reaction involves a gas, increasing the pressure of the gas has the same effect. The higher the pressure, the faster the reaction.

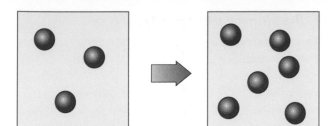

More particles means more collisions.

Measuring rate of reaction

We can follow the rate of a reaction by measuring the disappearance of the reactants or the appearance of the products.

When marble chippings (calcium carbonate) and dilute hydrochloric acid react together, carbon dioxide gas is given off. The volume of this gas can be measured at time intervals. This gives a measure of how fast the reaction is going. The solid line on the graph shows the measurements taken during an experiment using this reaction.

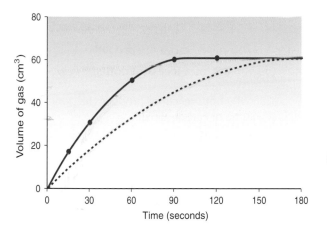

At first the curve rises steeply. The rate of reaction is fast. The concentration of the acid decreases as it is used up in the reaction. This makes the reaction go slower. Eventually all the acid is used up, and the reaction stops. Some marble chippings are left unreacted.

How science works

How could you find out if the data in this graph is reliable?

The reaction is repeated using the same volume of hydrochloric acid but with an equal volume of water added. So the same amount of acid was used, but at half the original concentration. These results are shown by the dotted line on the graph. With a lower concentration the reaction is slower. The dotted line is less steep and takes longer to become horizontal.

The rate of reaction can be calculated at any point by measuring the slope of the graph. The rate is a measure of volume divided by time.

Exam tip

You will be expected to be able to calculate a rate of reaction from a graph or figures in a table. It is worth practising this skill.

Catalysts

A catalyst is a substance that changes the rate of a reaction but is unchanged at the end of the reaction. Because it is not used up during the reaction, only a small amount of catalyst is needed to catalyse large amounts of reactants. The catalyst makes the reaction go quicker, but does not affect the quantity of the products made. A catalyst is often specific to a particular reaction.

When hydrogen peroxide decomposes, oxygen gas is released. This reaction is catalysed by solid manganese(IV) oxide. The graph shows the volume of oxygen gas given off during a reaction using 25 cm³ of hydrogen peroxide and 0.2 g of manganese(IV) oxide.

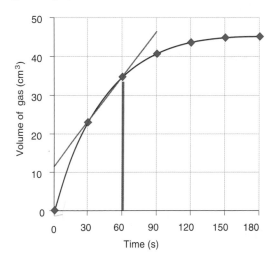

Surface area

For reactions that involve a solid, the rate of reaction is also affected by the size of the solid lumps used. The graph below shows the results of two experiments carried out at the same temperature, using the same mass of marble (calcium carbonate) and the same volume and concentration of hydrochloric acid. In one experiment powdered marble is used and in the other a lump of marble.

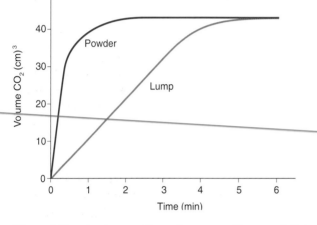

The red line is steeper than the green line, and this reaction is finished in a shorter time, showing that the powder reacted faster than the lump. For the same mass, the powder has a larger **surface area** than the lump. This is shown in the diagram.

If the limestone is crushed, the surface area is bigger because more surface is exposed

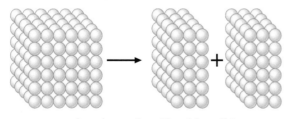

In each case, the acid particles collide with the limestone more frequently, and so the reaction will get faster

Because the powder has more surface area than the lump, the frequency of collisions with particles of acid is greater. This results in a faster reaction.

Exam tip

Make sure that you can explain why changes in temperature, concentration and surface area cause changes in rate of reaction.

Exploding custard

An **explosion** is a very fast reaction which releases a large volume of gaseous products. If a fine powder of a combustible solid is mixed with air, and a flame applied, an explosion may result. This can happen with solids such as coal dust, flour and even custard. Care has to be taken in coal mines, flour mills and custard factories to prevent a build up of dust in the air.

How science works

Even though care is taken, explosions sometimes happen in coal mines. Miners are in danger of injury from these explosions. Despite this danger, large quantities of coal are still mined.

Suggest why this is.

Test yourself

1 Explain why, in a reaction involving gases, increasing pressure increases the rate of reaction.

2 Look at the graph for the reaction rate investigation (page 25). When is the rate of reaction highest?

3 Explain why both reactions produce the same final volume of carbon dioxide.

4 Calculate the rate of the reaction shown by the solid line between 30 and 60 seconds.

5 Sketch a graph to show how the rate of this reaction would change if it was carried out at a higher temperature.

6 Look at the graph for the catalyst investigation (page 25). What total volume of oxygen was collected when the reaction had finished?

7 How can you tell from the graph that the reaction is faster after 30 s than it is after 60 s?

8 Comment on, and give an explanation for, the amount of product formed in the two reactions of the surface area investigation.

9 Copy the graph of reaction times above left and sketch on it the results you would expect using several smaller lumps of marble. (The total mass is unchanged.)

C3a What are atoms like?

After revising this item you should:

● be able to describe what is inside an atom, the connection between electronic structure and the Periodic Table and the structure of isotopes.

Atomic structure

An **atom** is made up from:

● **electrons** – arranged around the nucleus in a number of electron shells which are further and further out from the nucleus

● **protons** and **neutrons** – in the nucleus in the centre of the atom. The only atom that does not have any neutrons is the simplest form of hydrogen.

This diagram shows the structure of a sodium atom.

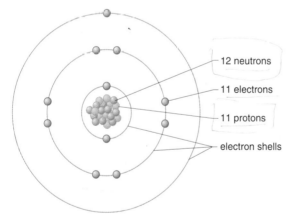

- 12 neutrons
- 11 electrons
- 11 protons
- electron shells

Inside a sodium atom.

Electrons, protons and neutrons have different properties.

Particle	Where found	Relative mass (mass compared with a proton)	Relative charge
proton	in nucleus	1	+1
neutron	in nucleus	1	0
electron	outside nucleus	0.0005	−1

The atom is neutral because the number of protons (positive charges) equals the number of electrons (negative charges).

Atomic number and mass number

The **atomic number** is the number of protons in an atom. The **mass number** is the total number of protons plus neutrons in an atom.

The shorthand way of writing an atom to show the number of nuclear particles is to put the mass number at the top left and the atomic number at the bottom left of the symbol. So $^{27}_{13}\text{Al}$ shows that an atom of aluminium has 13 protons and 27 − 13 = 14 neutrons.

Isotopes

Each atom of the same element has the same number of protons. But in many elements some of the atoms have different numbers of neutrons.

Atoms of the same element with different mass numbers are called **isotopes**.

Because mass number is number of protons + neutrons, isotopes are also atoms of the same element that have different numbers of neutrons. The table shows the number of protons and neutrons in two isotopes of chlorine.

Isotope	Chlorine-35	Chlorine-37
number of protons	17	17
number of neutrons	18	20
mass number	35	37

Exam tip

You can find the number of neutrons by subtracting the proton number from the mass number.

From this information you can work out the number of protons (and therefore electrons).

Isotopes can be written using the atomic symbols.

We can write chlorine-37 as $^{37}_{17}Cl$. The relative molecular mass of chlorine is 35.5 because natural chlorine is a mixture of 75 per cent chlorine-35 and 25 per cent chlorine-37.

Test yourself

1 An atom of phosphorus has 15 protons and 16 neutrons. What is the mass number of this phosphorus atom?

2 Work out how many protons, neutrons and electrons there are in these particles:

   (a) $^{65}_{30}Zn$
   (b) $^{108}_{47}Ag$
   (c) $^{39}_{19}K$.

3 Two isotopes of bromine are $^{79}_{35}Br$ and $^{81}_{35}Br$. State three things that are the same in both these atoms and one thing that is different.

4 Write the symbol for the isotope of calcium which has 26 neutrons.

C3b Ionic bonding & C3c Covalent bonding and the Periodic Table

After revising these items you should:

● be able to describe how ionic and covalent compounds are formed, explain their properties and describe how the electronic structure of an atom is related to the Periodic Table.

Ionic bonding

Positive ions:

● Formed when an atom loses one or more electrons.

● E.g. sodium forms a sodium ion when a sodium atom loses one electron (e⁻ is the symbol for an electron).

$$Na - e^- \longrightarrow Na^+$$

● E.g. magnesium forms a magnesium ion when a magnesium atom loses two electrons.

$$Mg - 2e^- \longrightarrow Mg^{2+}$$

Negative ions:

● Formed when an atom gains one or more electrons.

● E.g. chlorine forms a chloride ion when a chlorine atom gains one electron.

$$Cl + e^- \longrightarrow Cl^-$$

● E.g. oxygen forms an oxide ion when an oxygen atom gains two electrons.

$$O + 2e^- \longrightarrow O^{2-}$$

When a metal combines with a non-metal, one or more electrons move from the metal atom to the non-metal atom. The positive and negative ions formed then attract each other. This attraction between positive and negative charges forms the **ionic bond**.

Exam tip

Remember that a covalent compound is formed between non-metals only. An ionic compound is formed between a metal and a non-metal.

Dot and cross diagrams for ionic bonding

The transfer of electrons from the metal atom to the non-metal atom always results in both ions having a complete outer shell. This is called a **stable octet**.

Each ion formed has the same electron arrangement as a noble gas:

● Neon arrangement for the sodium ion.

● Argon arrangement for the chloride ion.

We can use dots and crosses to represent electrons and show how the ions are formed.

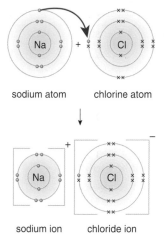

sodium atom   chlorine atom

↓

sodium ion   chloride ion

Dot and cross diagram for sodium chloride.

You need to work out the following dot and cross diagrams.

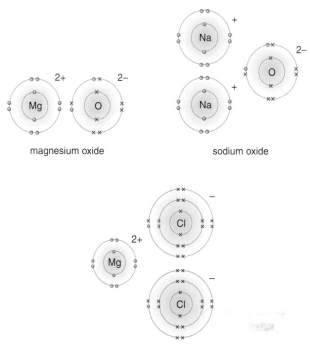

magnesium oxide   sodium oxide

magnesium chloride

From ions to formulae

You can use the charges on the ions to work out the formulae of **ionic compounds**. The total positive charge must equal the total negative charge so that there is no overall charge on the compound. For example:

- Magnesium chloride – the ions are Mg^{2+} and Cl^-. To make the charges equal you need two Cl^- ions. So the formula is $MgCl_2$.
- Sodium oxide – the ions are Na^+ and O^{2-}. You need two sodium ions for every oxide so the formula is Na_2O.

Properties of ionic compounds

The following table summarises the properties of ionic compounds, e.g. sodium chloride and magnesium oxide.

electricity conduction	do not conduct when solid – the ions cannot move
	do conduct when molten – the ions are free to move
structure	the ions are arranged regularly in a giant **ionic lattice**
	the positive and negative ions are held together by a strong **electrostatic attraction**
	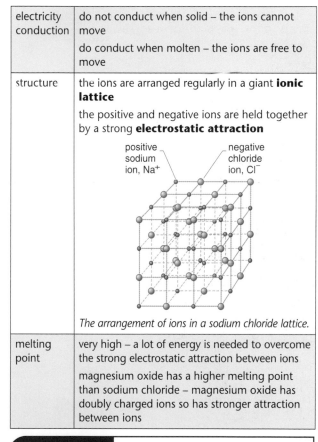 *The arrangement of ions in a sodium chloride lattice.*
melting point	very high – a lot of energy is needed to overcome the strong electrostatic attraction between ions
	magnesium oxide has a higher melting point than sodium chloride – magnesium oxide has doubly charged ions so has stronger attraction between ions

Covalent bonding

Features of **covalent bonding** are shown in the diagram.

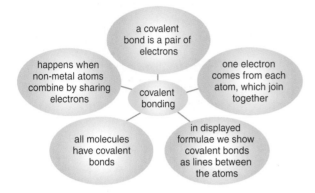

The diagram shows how covalent bond formation is represented.

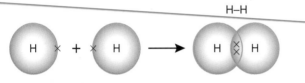

Dot and cross diagrams for covalent bonding

The diagrams below show how the pairs of electrons are shared between each atom. Each atom combines so that it has a full outer shell of eight electrons (a stable octet). The exception is hydrogen which has a full outer shell with two electrons.

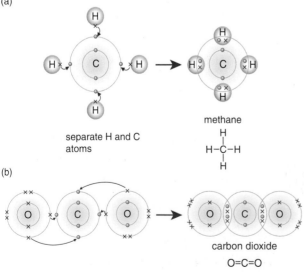

Dot and cross diagrams for covalent bonding in (a) methane and (b) carbon dioxide.

In order to get eight electrons around each atom, you sometimes have to pair up two sets of electrons to form a double bond.

Properties of molecular structures

The following table summarises the properties of simple covalent molecules, e.g. carbon dioxide and water.

electricity conduction	do not conduct – have no ions and so their electrons cannot move outside their molecules
melting point and boiling point	low – due to weak **intermolecular forces** between the **molecules** (most small molecules are gases or liquids)

The Periodic Table

The Periodic Table shows the elements in order of increasing atomic number. It gives the mass number and atomic number of each element.

The elements in the Periodic Table are arranged in columns and rows. The columns are called **Groups**. The rows are called **Periods**. All the elements in a row are in the same Period.

The diagram shows a shortened version of the Periodic Table.

1	2	3	4	5	6	7	8
1 **H** Hydrogen 1							4 **He** Helium 2
7 **Li** Lithium 3	9 **Be** Beryllium 4	11 **B** Boron 5	12 **C** Carbon 6	14 **N** Nitrogen 7	16 **O** Oxygen 8	19 **F** Fluorine 9	20 **Ne** Neon 10
23 **Na** Sodium 11	24 **Mg** Magnesium 12	27 **Al** Aluminium 13	28 **Si** Silicon 14	31 **P** Phosphorus 15	32 **S** Sulfur 16	35.5 **Cl** Chlorine 17	40 **Ar** Argon 18
39 **K** Potassium 19	40 **Ca** Calcium 20	70 **Ga** Galium 31	73 **Ge** Germanium 32	75 **As** Arsenic 33	79 **Se** Selenium 34	80 **Br** Bromine 35	84 **Kr** Krypton 36

Electronic structure

Each electron shell can hold only a certain number of electrons:

- The shell nearest the nucleus (the first shell) can hold a maximum of two electrons.
- The second and third shells can hold a maximum of eight electrons.

The shells are filled in order starting with the lowest. The table shows you how to write electronic structures.

Element	Number of electrons	Electronic structure
hydrogen	1	1
helium	2	2
lithium	3	2.1
beryllium	4	2.2
boron	5	2.3
fluorine	9	2.7
neon	10	2.8
sodium	11	2.8.1

Exam tip

You do not have to learn the electronic structures of the first 20 elements but you must be able to work them out using a Periodic Table. Remember that the number of electrons and the number of protons are the same in the neutral atom.

Electronic structure and the Periodic Table

The electronic structure of an atom shows which Group and Period it belongs to, e.g the diagram shows sodium which is in Group 1 and Period 3.

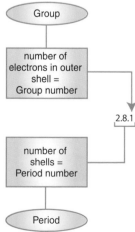

Group

number of electrons in outer shell = Group number

2.8.1

number of shells = Period number

Period

Test yourself

1 (a) Which of these substances are ionic compounds?
       carbon monoxide (CO)   potassium chloride (KCl)   methane (CH_4)   magnesium chloride ($MgCl_2$)   sodium bromide (NaBr)
   (b) For each ionic compound, write down the formula of each ion present.

2 Construct dot and cross diagrams for:
   (a) water
   (b) chlorine
   (c) methane
   (d) carbon dioxide.

3 Write the formulae for:
   (a) magnesium oxide
   (b) calcium chloride
   (c) iron(III) chloride
   (d) lithium oxide.

   Use these symbols for the ions to help you: Mg^{2+}, Ca^{2+}, Fe^{3+}, Li^+, O^{2-}, Cl^-.

4 Molten (liquid) sodium bromide conducts electricity but water does not. Explain this difference.

5 An atom has the electronic structure 2.8.5. Which Group and Period does this atom belong to?

C3d The Group 1 elements

After revising this item you should:

- be able to explain why the Group 1 metals react in a similar way, why their reactivity increases down the Group and how to identify their ions using a flame test.

Very reactive metals

All Group 1 metals (**alkali metals**) have similar properties and react in a similar way.

As we go **down** Group 1, the metals become **more** reactive.

The difference in reactivity is best observed by comparing the reactions of small cubes of lithium, sodium and potassium with water, as shown in the diagram.

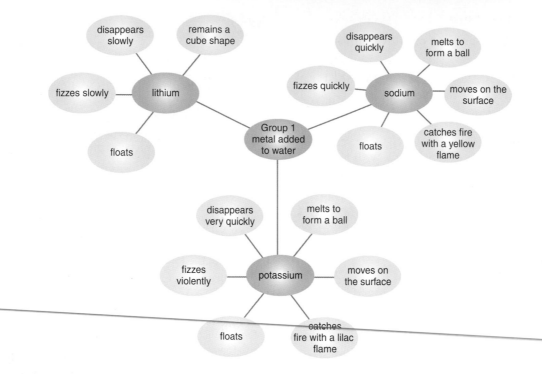

The fizzing is caused by the bubbles of hydrogen gas which are formed in this reaction. If universal indicator is added to the water, the indicator changes to purple. This shows that the reaction makes an alkali – which is why we call the Group 1 elements alkali metals.

Exam tip

The word 'observation' means what you see, hear or feel. If an exam question asks about observations, you will not get marks if you write things like 'hydrogen given off' or 'reacts rapidly'.

The reason for the difference in reactivity is to do with how easy it is to lose the outer electron. The more reactive the Group 1 metal, the easier it is to lose the outer electron from an atom and form a stable ion. So the more reactive the metal, the more easily it is oxidised.

How science works

Mendeleev published his Periodic Table in 1869. Sodium and potassium were isolated in 1807 and lithium was detected in 1817.

Rubidium and caesium were not detected until 1860. Why did it take so long to detect the last two?

Predicting the properties of Group 1 metals

The properties of the Group 1 metals show trends (gradual changes) down the group. The table shows the trends in melting point, hardness and reactivity with oxygen.

You should be able to predict the properties of the other Group 1 metals from a table like this. For example, the melting point of lithium must be at least 30–40°C higher than sodium if you follow the figures.

Metal	Melting point (°C)	Hardness	Reactivity with oxygen
sodium	98	fairly soft	burns steadily when heated
potassium	64	soft	burns rapidly when heated
rubidium	39	very soft	catches fire without heating

Exam tip

When predicting a property of an alkali metal, first look at your Periodic Table to see where it is in the Group, then look to see which way the trend in this property is going.

Group 1 metals react in a similar way because:

- they all have one electron in their outer shell
- when they react, their atoms lose this electron
- an ion with a single positive charge is formed
- this ion has a stable electronic structure (full outer shell).

For sodium, the ionic equation for this 'half reaction' is written:

$$Na - e^- \longrightarrow Na^+$$

We call loss of electrons **oxidation**.

You can see from the ionic equation that this is an oxidation reaction because an electron is lost.

Making alkalis

The alkali formed when a Group 1 metal reacts with water is an alkali metal hydroxide, e.g. sodium hydroxide, potassium hydroxide. The alkali metal hydroxide dissolves in the water as the reaction occurs. The other product of the reaction is hydrogen.

Word equations and balanced symbol equations for the reaction of alkali metals with water follow a pattern:

$$2M + 2H_2O \longrightarrow 2MOH + H_2$$

alkali metal + water $\longrightarrow$ metal hydroxide + hydrogen

(where M is the alkali metal).

So the equation for the reaction between lithium and water is:

$$2Li + 2H_2O \longrightarrow 2LiOH + H_2$$

lithium + water $\longrightarrow$ lithium hydroxide + hydrogen

Flame tests

We can find out which Group 1 metal is present in an alkali metal compound by carrying out a **flame test**, as follows:

1 Moisten a flame test wire.
2 Dip the end of the wire into a sample of the solid alkali metal compound.
3 Put the sample on the wire into a blue Bunsen flame.
4 Observe the colour of the flame.

The flame test shows the alkali metal present in the alkali metal compound because each metal gives a distinctive colour.

C3e The Group 7 elements

Halogens

The elements in Group 7 of the Periodic Table are called the **halogens**. They include:

- fluorine
- chlorine
- bromine
- iodine

As you go down the Group from chlorine to iodine the halogens change in appearance. At room temperature:

- chlorine is a light green gas
- bromine is a deep orange liquid
- iodine is a grey solid.

Halogens and alkali metals

The word equations and balanced symbol equations for the reaction of halogens with alkali metals follow a pattern:

halogen + alkali metal $\longrightarrow$ alkali metal **halide**

So for the reaction between potassium and chlorine:

$2K$ + Cl_2 $\longrightarrow$ $2KCl$
potassium + chlorine $\longrightarrow$ potassium chloride

Exam tip

Note how the name of the halogen changes in the compound. The -ine at the end of the halogen name changes to -ide when we name the compound.

For example, the element iodine is a halogen but the compound potassium iodide is an alkali metal halide.

Displacing halogens

The reactivity of the halogens decreases down the group. You can see this by looking at how halogens react with solutions of alkali metal halides. These reactions are called **displacement** reactions.

In class experiments the halogens are added as their solutions in water. The table shows the reaction between different halogens and sodium halides. The ticks show where there is a reaction.

Halogen	Halide solution		
	sodium chloride	sodium bromide	sodium iodide
chlorine	✗	✓	✓
bromine	✗	✗	✓
iodine	✗	✗	✗

You can see that the halogen reacts with the halide only when the halide is lower in the Group than the halogen.

- You can tell when there is a reaction because the colour of the solution changes.
- Alkali metal halides are colourless but the halogens are coloured.

We can write equations for these displacement reactions as follows:

Cl_2	+	$2NaBr$	$\longrightarrow$	Br_2	+	$2NaCl$
chlorine	+	sodium bromide	$\longrightarrow$	bromine	+	sodium chloride
(green)		(colourless)		(orange solution)		(colourless)

Exam tip

You only have to learn one equation for the reactions of the halogen with the halides because they follow a general pattern. Remember that the halogens are always diatomic (written with a 2 at the bottom right).

Reactivity decreases down the Group

The displacement reactions show that the halogens get less reactive as you go down the Group.

The reason for this is to do with how easy it is for a halogen atom to gain an outer electron and form a stable ion with eight outer electrons.

The more reactive the halogen, the easier it is to gain an outer electron. So the more reactive the halogen, the more easily it is reduced.

Properties of the halogens

The halogens have similar properties and react in a similar way. This is because:

- they all have seven electrons in their outer shell
- when they react, their atoms gain one electron
- an ion with a single negative charge is formed
- this ion has a stable electronic structure (full outer shell).

For chlorine, the ionic equation for this 'half reaction' is written:

$$Cl + e^- \longrightarrow Cl^-$$

Gain of electrons is called **reduction**. You can see from this ionic equation that this is a reduction reaction because an electron is gained.

> ### Exam tip
>
> Use the mnemonic **OIL RIG** to remember if oxidation or reduction takes place. **O**xidation **I**s **L**oss (of electrons); **R**eduction **I**s **G**ain (of electrons).

Predicting halogen properties

The properties of the halogens show trends (gradual changes) down the group. You should be able to predict the properties of the other halogens from a table like the following.

For example, the colour of fluorine must be lighter in colour than chlorine – it is yellow. If you follow the pattern of the figures fluorine must have a boiling point much lower than chlorine.

Halogen	Boiling point (°C)	State	Colour
chlorine	−34	gas	light green
bromine	+59	liquid	deep orange (reddish-brown)
iodine	+187	solid	dark grey

> ### Exam tip
>
> When predicting a property of a halogen, first look at your Periodic Table to see where it is in the Group, then look to see which way the trend in this property is going.

> ### How science works
>
> Elements with very high atomic numbers can only be made in atomic reactors. Some scientists think that it may be possible to make a halogen below astatine in the Periodic Table.
>
> Suggest why this element has not yet been made.

> ### Test yourself
>
> 1 Why is there no reaction between sodium bromide and iodine?
>
> 2 Both chlorine and bromine react with sodium. Which one reacts most vigorously?
>
> 3 Write a balanced symbol equation for the reaction of iodine with potassium.
>
> 4 Look at the table above showing the boiling point, state and colour of the halogens. Astatine is below iodine in Group 7. Predict the boiling point, state and colour of astatine.
>
> 5 Write a balanced symbol equation for the reaction of chlorine with sodium iodide.

C3f Electrolysis

After revising this item you should:

- be able to explain what happens during the electrolysis of dilute sulfuric acid and how electrolysis is used in the extraction of aluminium.

Dilute sulfuric acid electrolysis

Sulfuric acid is broken down by electrolysis into hydrogen and oxygen.

- Hydrogen bubbles off at the cathode.
- Oxygen bubbles off at the anode.

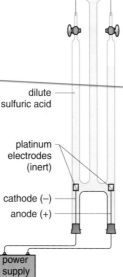

oxygen collected here
hydrogen collected here
dilute sulfuric acid
platinum electrodes (inert)
cathode (−)
anode (+)
power supply

Electrode reactions

The ions present in sulfuric acid are OH^-, H^+ and SO_4^{2-}. During electrolysis the hydrogen ions move towards the cathode because it is negatively charged. They take up electrons from the cathode and become hydrogen atoms. These join up to form molecules of hydrogen gas.

$$2H^+ + 2e^- \longrightarrow H_2$$

The hydroxide ions (which come from the water) and the sulfate ions move towards the anode because it is positively charged. The hydroxide ions give up their electrons to the anode and form molecules of oxygen gas.

$$4OH^- \longrightarrow 2H_2O + O_2 + 4e^-$$

The sulfate ions remain in solution because they do not give off electrons as easily as hydroxide ions.

Extracting aluminium

Reactive metals such as aluminium are found in the rocks as minerals. The aluminium is present in the bauxite ore as the compound aluminium oxide.

We can purify the bauxite and use the pure molten aluminium oxide as the electrolyte in an electrolysis cell. The anodes and cathode in this cell are made of a type of carbon called **graphite**.

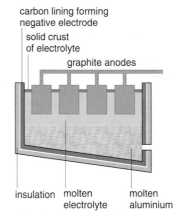

carbon lining forming negative electrode
solid crust of electrolyte
graphite anodes
insulation | molten electrolyte | molten aluminium

An electrolysis cell used in the manufacture of aluminium.

This electrolysis needs a large amount of electrical energy to work. A large electric current is passed through molten aluminium oxide. This keeps the aluminium oxide molten as well as decomposing it into aluminium and oxygen. The equation for this is:

$2Al_2O_3$	$\longrightarrow$	$4Al$	$+$	$3O_2$
aluminium oxide	$\longrightarrow$	aluminium	$+$	oxygen

Aluminium is expensive to produce because the process uses a large amount of electricity. Cryolite is added to the aluminium oxide to lower its melting point, which helps to reduce the amount of electricity used.

Electrode reactions in electrolysis

The ions present in molten aluminium oxide are Al^{3+} and O^{2-}. During electrolysis aluminium ions move towards the cathode. Here, they take up electrons from the cathode and become aluminium atoms.

$$Al^{3+} + 3e^- \longrightarrow Al$$

The oxide ions move towards the anode. Here, they give up their electrons to the anode and form oxygen atoms. These join together to form molecules of oxygen gas.

$$2O^{2-} - 4e^- \longrightarrow O_2$$

The oxygen reacts with the hot graphite anodes. The anodes get smaller and smaller because they are oxidised to carbon dioxide gas which escapes into the air.

This means that the anodes have to be replaced frequently.

Test yourself

1   Aluminium oxide is an ionic compound. Why does aluminium oxide need to be molten for it to be electrolysed?

2   The overall equation for the electrolysis of sulfuric acid is $2H_2O \longrightarrow 2H_2 + O_2$.

    What does this equation tell you about the number of hydrogen molecules formed compared with the number of oxygen molecules?

3   Aluminium is extracted from an electrolyte mixture of cryolite and aluminium oxide at about 1000°C. It is theoretically possible to extract aluminium by heating aluminium oxide with carbon at temperatures above 2500°C. Suggest why this is not done.

4   Is the following electrode reaction oxidation or reduction? Explain your answer.
    $$2O^{2-} - 4e^- \longrightarrow O_2$$

C3g Transition elements & C3h Metal structure and properties

After revising these items you should:

● be able to describe how metallic bonding explains the properties of metals and describe some properties of transition elements and their compounds.

Transition elements and their compounds

The **transition elements** are metals which are found together in a block in the middle of the Periodic Table.

Transition elements and their compounds are often catalysts. For example:

• iron in the Haber Process
• nickel in the manufacture of margarine.

Unlike other metal compounds, **transition metal** compounds are usually coloured.

• Copper compounds are blue.
• Iron(II) compounds are light green.
• Iron(III) compounds are orange or brown.

Breaking down transition metal carbonates

Thermal decomposition is a reaction in which a compound is broken down into at least two other substances by heat. When transition metal carbonates are decomposed by heat a metal oxide (solid) and carbon dioxide (gas) are formed. The metal oxide is usually a different colour from the metal carbonate.

$$CuCO_3 \rightarrow CuO + CO_2$$

copper(II) carbonate	$\rightarrow$	copper(II) oxide	+	carbon dioxide

Exam tip

You only have to learn one symbol equation for the thermal decomposition of transition metal carbonates because they are exactly the same, except for the symbol of the metal.

Identifying ions

We can test for many ions by **precipitation** reactions. These reactions occur when two solutions react to form an insoluble solid (the **precipitate**). When sodium hydroxide solution is added to a solution of a transition element compound a precipitate is formed.

The colour of this precipitate can be used to identify the transition metal ion in solution.

- Copper(II) ions, Cu^{2+}, give a blue precipitate.
- Iron(II) ions, Fe^{2+}, give a grey-green precipitate.
- Iron(III) ions, Fe^{3+}, give an orange-brown precipitate.

We can write ionic equations for the reactions between sodium hydroxide and copper(II), iron(II) and iron(III) ions. They follow a similar pattern. One hydroxide ion is needed for each positive charge on the metal ion.

$$Cu^{2+} + 2OH^- \rightarrow Cu(OH)_2$$

copper(II) ion	+	hydroxide ion	$\rightarrow$	copper hydroxide

$$Fe^{3+} + 3OH^- \rightarrow Fe(OH)_3$$

iron(III) ion	+	hydroxide ion	$\rightarrow$	iron(III) hydroxide

Exam tip

Make a list of all the tests for gases and ions you come across (e.g. carbon dioxide and copper(II) ions). Test yourself on these regularly by using flash cards or getting someone else to test you.

Metallic bonds

The particles in a metal are held close together by **metallic bonding**, in which a lattice of positive metal ions is held together by a 'sea' of electrons. These electrons are described as free, mobile or delocalised because they can move throughout the metal. There is a strong electrostatic attraction between the 'sea' of delocalised electrons and close packed positive metal ions.

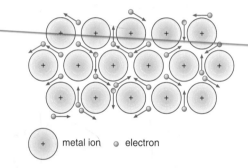

+ metal ion　　○ electron

Metallic bonding.

Exam tip

Remember that only some of the electrons in the metal structure are able to move. It is a common mistake to think that the lattice consists of atomic nuclei rather than positive ions and that all the electrons move.

Explaining the properties of metals

Metallic bonding is responsible for giving metals many of their typical properties:

- High melting and boiling points – due to strong forces of attraction between the delocalised electrons and the positive metal ions (cations). It takes a lot of energy to overcome these forces of attraction.
- Good electricity conduction – because the delocalised electrons are free to move past the regular arrangement of metal cations when the metal is connected to a power supply.

We can explain why some metals are suited to a particular use using this model. For example:

- metals which have higher tensile strength must have stronger forces of attraction between the metal cations and the delocalised electrons
- metals which are better conductors must have electrons which move more easily.

Exam tip

You will be expected to explain why metals are suited for particular uses. To do this you will also need to remember the typical properties of metals.

How science works

Safraz and Peter investigate the strength of pieces of a metal wire. They add weights to the wire until it breaks. Safraz adds 2 kg masses at a time and Peter adds 1 kg masses.

The table shows their results using a constant length of wire.

	Safraz			Peter				
	1st run	2nd run	3rd run	1st run	2nd run	3rd run	4th run	5th run
diameter of wire X (mm)	0.8	0.8	0.7	0.7	0.8	0.8	0.8	0.7
breaking mass (kg)	98	94	86	89	95	93	94	86

Comment on the validity and reliability of both sets of results.

Superconductors

Most substances have some resistance to the flow of electricity through them, but some materials can conduct electricity with little or no resistance. These are called **superconductors**.

Superconductors are used to:

- make powerful electromagnets
- make superfast electronic circuits
- transmit power with minimum energy loss.

The problem with many superconductors is that they only work at extremely low temperatures. That is why scientists are interested in developing superconductors which can work at 20°C.

How science works

Superconductors can transmit power with minimum energy loss, but they work only at very low temperatures. In recent years superconductors have been developed which work at slightly higher temperatures but not at normal air temperature.

An electricity company which is losing money because of power losses wants to invest into research into superconductors. Is this a sensible thing to do?

Test yourself

1 Compound X decomposes to form an oxide and carbon dioxide. The oxide reacts with an acid to form a solution which gives a grey-green precipitate, when sodium hydroxide is added. State the name of compound X.

2 Write an ionic equation for the reaction of iron(II) ions with sodium hydroxide ions.

3 State two ways in which metallic bonding differs from ionic bonding.

4 Titanium is stronger than magnesium. Use ideas about metallic bonding to explain this difference.

5 The information in the table compares the properties of three metals.

Metal	Melting point (°C)	Density (g/cm^3)	Electrical conductivity	Tensile strength
copper	1083	8.92	very good	medium
lead	328	11.34	good	low
iron	1535	7.87	good	very high

(a) Explain why copper is the best of these metals to use for electrical wiring.
(b) Explain why iron is the best of these metals for making a car body.

C4a Acids and bases

After revising this item you should:

● understand how acids are neutralised by bases and carbonates and know about salt formation during neutralisation, with equations

The pH scale

The **pH** scale shows how strongly acidic or alkaline a substance is. The pH value of a solution can be measured using universal indicator paper or solution. The colour of the universal indicator changes according to the pH value.

You can also find the pH value using a pH meter or a pH probe connected to a datalogger.

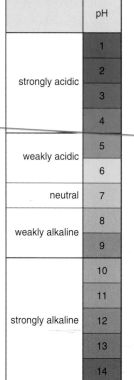

	pH
strongly acidic	1
	2
	3
	4
weakly acidic	5
	6
neutral	7
weakly alkaline	8
	9
strongly alkaline	10
	11
	12
	13
	14

Acids, alkalis and bases

The common laboratory acids are:

● hydrochloric acid
● sulfuric acid
● nitric acid.

All acids in solution in water contain hydrogen ions, H^+.

A **base** is a substance which neutralises an acid. Bases are often solids.

Examples of bases are:

● metal oxides, such as magnesium oxide
● metal hydroxides.

A base which dissolves in water is called an **alkali**. Many hydroxides, e.g. sodium hydroxide and calcium hydroxide, are alkalis.

All alkalis in solution in water contain hydroxide ions, OH^-.

Neutralisation

The equation for a **neutralisation** reaction is:

$$\text{acid} + \text{base} \longrightarrow \text{salt} + \text{water}$$

Water and most salt solutions are neutral. When a base reacts with an acid, the pH of the solution rises until there is no acid left. At this point the alkali has exactly reacted with the acid and you are left with only salt and water. The solution is neutral.

We can describe the neutralisation of an acid with an alkali by an ionic equation:

$$H^+ + OH^- \longrightarrow H_2O$$

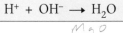

When metal oxide and hydroxides neutralise acids they form salts. The name of the salt formed comes partly from the metal and partly from the acid. For example:

● hydrochloric acid forms metal chlorides
● nitric acid forms metal nitrates
● sulfuric acid forms metal sulfates.

Equations for acid–base reactions

Metal oxides and hydroxides react with acids to form a salt and water:

$$\underset{\substack{\text{sulfuric}\\\text{acid}}}{H_2SO_4} + \underset{\substack{\text{copper(II)}\\\text{oxide}}}{CuO} \longrightarrow \underset{\substack{\text{copper(II)}\\\text{sulfate}}}{CuSO_4} + \underset{\text{water}}{H_2O}$$

$$\underset{\substack{\text{sulfuric}\\\text{acid}}}{H_2SO_4} + \underset{\substack{\text{sodium}\\\text{hydroxide}}}{2NaOH} \longrightarrow \underset{\substack{\text{sodium}\\\text{sulfate}}}{Na_2SO_4} + \underset{\text{water}}{2H_2O}$$

$$\underset{\substack{\text{nitric}\\\text{acid}}}{HNO_3} + \underset{\substack{\text{ammonia}\\\text{solution}}}{NH_3} \longrightarrow \underset{\substack{\text{ammonium}\\\text{nitrate}}}{NH_4NO_3}$$

Exam tip

Make sure that you can write the equations for the reactions of the three main acids with ammonia and metal hydroxides. Note that with ammonia there is no water on the right of the equation.

Metal carbonates neutralise acids to form a salt, water and carbon dioxide.

$$Na_2CO_3 + 2HCl \rightarrow 2NaCl + H_2O + CO_2$$

sodium carbonate + hydro-chloric acid → sodium chloride + water + carbon dioxide

Test yourself

1 Name the salts formed when:

   (a) calcium carbonate reacts with nitric acid
   (b) copper oxide reacts with sulfuric acid.

2 Describe how and explain why the pH changes when a solution of hydrochloric acid is gradually added to a solution of sodium hydroxide.

3 Write the simplest ionic equation for the reaction between hydrochloric acid and sodium hydroxide.

4 Write a balanced equation for the reaction between calcium carbonate and nitric acid.

5 Write a balanced equation for the reaction of ammonia with sulfuric acid.

C4b Reacting masses & C4c Fertilisers and crop yield

After revising these items you should:

● understand why mass is conserved, know how to work out masses of reactants, products and percentage yield in a reaction and understand the reasons for using fertilisers and some problems caused by their use.

Relative atomic mass and relative formula mass

Relative formula mass (M_r) is found by adding together the **relative atomic masses** (A_r) of each atom.

Here are some examples:

A_r	Working out M_r
Na = 23, Br = 80	NaBr = 23 + 80 = M_r of 103
Mg = 24, Cl = 35.5	$MgCl_2$ = 24 + (2 × 35.5) = M_r of 95

Using brackets in formulae

Sometimes, particular atoms are paired together, e.g. OH and SO_4. You should learn to recognise these groups.

If there is more than one of these groups in a compound, they are bracketed, e.g. $Fe(OH)_2$. The 2 here multiplies whatever is in the brackets. So the M_r of this compound is worked out like this:

A_r: Fe = 56, O = 16, H = 1
$Fe(OH)_2$ has one Fe, two Os and two Hs.
So the M_r is 56 + 2 × (16 + 1) = 90.

Exam tip

If the formula has a group in brackets, it is easier to work out the formula mass inside the brackets first, then multiply by the number outside the brackets.

Masses of reactants and products

When a reaction takes place, the atoms rearrange to form the new products. No atoms are gained or lost, so the total mass of the reactants is the same as the total mass of the products. We say that the mass is conserved.

$$2Mg + O_2 \rightarrow 2MgO$$
reactants   product

In this equation:

● there are two atoms of magnesium and two atoms of oxygen in the reactants
● there is the same number of atoms in the product.

Exam tip

Remember that a number in front of a formula multiplies all the way through the formula.

Calculating masses of reactants or products

If we use a greater mass of reactants we get a greater mass of products. This is true as long as the mass of all the reactants is greater.

You can use simple maths to calculate the mass of the product obtained from a given amount of reactant. For example:

When 48 g of magnesium react with 32 g of oxygen, 80 g of magnesium oxide is made.

How many grams of magnesium oxide can be made from 12 g of magnesium?

48 g of magnesium give 80 g of magnesium oxide, so 12 g of magnesium make $(12 \div 48) \times 80 = 20$ g of magnesium oxide.

Even if you are not told the amounts of reactants and products you can still work out the amount of product from a given mass of reactant. You will need to know the equation. First work out the relative formula masses, then multiply these by the numbers in front of the formulae. For example:

Calculate the mass of water formed when 4 g of methane (CH_4) are burned. (C = 12, H = 4, O = 16)

$$CH_4 \quad + \quad 2O_2 \quad \rightarrow \quad CO_2 \quad + \quad 2H_2O$$
$$12 + (4 \times 1) \qquad \text{gives} \qquad\qquad 2 \times (2 + 16)$$

16 g of methane   gives   36 g of water

So 4 g of methane   gives $\dfrac{4 \times 36}{16} = 9$ g of water

Exam tip

Always show your working in calculations. Put the relevant numbers below each compound in the equation so that you can clearly see which figures to use.

Yield

We can calculate the amount of product that we expect to get from the reactants. This is called the **predicted yield**. The amount of product we actually get by experiment is called the **actual yield**.

Chemists often use **percentage yield** as a way of comparing the amount of product made with amount expected.

We can calculate percentage yield by using the formula:

$$\text{percentage yield} = \frac{\text{actual yield}}{\text{predicted yield}} \times 100$$

A scientist calculates that 80 g of magnesium oxide should be formed when magnesium reacts with excess oxygen. An experiment shows that 48 g of magnesium oxide is formed.

The percentage yield is:

$$\frac{48}{80} \times 100 = 60\%$$

How science works

Kate prepared a sample of nickel sulfate by adding a calculated amount of sulfuric acid to a known amount of nickel carbonate. She heated the mixture for 10 minutes and then filtered it. The filtrate was left in the open air and allowed to crystallise.

The yield of crystals was much lower than expected. Suggest why.

What are fertilisers?

Fertilisers:

- increase the crop yield by replacing the **essential elements** (nitrogen, phosphorus and potassium) taken from the soil by crop plants
- provide extra amounts of nitrogen so that more of this element gets into plant proteins and increases crop growth
- are soluble in water so they are absorbed by plant roots.

How science works

When mixed with other chemicals, fertilisers can be explosive. Fertilisers are readily available from garden centres and farmers store large quantities of them.

Some people think that the Government should pass laws to make the sale of fertilisers more difficult. Give arguments for and against this suggestion.

Eutrophication

Eutrophication is the process by which lakes and rivers become 'dead' through pollution by fertilisers.

The diagram shows the process.

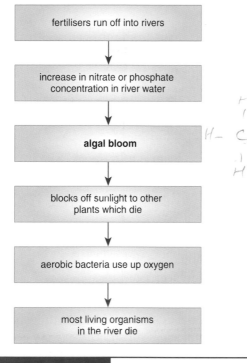

```
┌──────────────────────────────────┐
│   fertilisers run off into rivers │
└──────────────────────────────────┘
              │
              ▼
┌──────────────────────────────────┐
│  increase in nitrate or phosphate │
│    concentration in river water   │
└──────────────────────────────────┘
              │
              ▼
┌──────────────────────────────────┐
│            algal bloom            │
└──────────────────────────────────┘
              │
              ▼
┌──────────────────────────────────┐
│    blocks off sunlight to other   │
│        plants which die           │
└──────────────────────────────────┘
              │
              ▼
┌──────────────────────────────────┐
│   aerobic bacteria use up oxygen  │
└──────────────────────────────────┘
              │
              ▼
┌──────────────────────────────────┐
│      most living organisms        │
│        in the river die           │
└──────────────────────────────────┘
```

How science works

Organic wastes from farms such as manure, silage and vegetable washings are high in nitrogen and phosphorus. What should farmers do to make sure that these wastes do not cause eutrophication?

Calculating percentage mass

We can find the percentage of nitrogen in a fertiliser using the formula:

$$\frac{\text{total mass of nitrogen in fertiliser}}{\text{relative formula mass of fertiliser}} \times 100$$

So to find the percentage of nitrogen in ammonium nitrate (NH_4NO_3) using the atomic masses H = 1, N = 14, O = 16:

$$\frac{\text{two nitrogen atoms} \rightarrow 2 \times 14}{\text{M_r of ammonium nitrate} \rightarrow (2 \times 14) + (4 \times 1) + (3 \times 16)} = 35\%$$

You can do a similar calculation for other elements present in a compound.

Exam tip

Make sure that you know how to calculate the relative formula mass of fertilisers such as ammonium nitrate (NH_4NO_3) and ammonium sulfate (($NH_4)_2SO_4$) (see page 41).

Making fertilisers

Fertilisers are salts made by neutralising particular acids with particular alkalis.

Alkali used	Acid used	Fertiliser made
ammonia	nitric acid	ammonium nitrate
ammonia	phosphoric acid	ammonium phosphate
ammonia	sulfuric acid	ammonium sulfate
potassium hydroxide	nitric acid	potassium nitrate

We can make a fertiliser using a titration procedure:

1 Put acid into a flask using an accurate pipette or measuring cylinder.

2 Fill a burette with alkali.

3 Put a few drops of an indicator into the flask.

4 Add alkali from the burette until the indicator in the flask just changes colour.

5 Repeat the process without the indicator, adding the correct volume of alkali.

6 Evaporate off some of the water then leave to crystallise.

7 Separate off the crystals by **filtration**, then wash and dry them.

Exam tip

You should know the names of the acids and alkalis used to make particular fertilisers and realise that the indicator colour changes when the solution is neutral.

Test yourself

Look at the Periodic Table to find relative atomic masses.

1 Calculate the relative formula mass of:

(a) ammonium sulfate $(NH_4)_2SO_4$

(b) urea $(NH_2)_2CO$

2 When 8 g of sulfur burns in excess oxygen, 16 g of sulfur dioxide is formed. What mass of sulfur dioxide is formed when 40 g of sulfur is burned?

3 Amelia heated 10 g of calcium carbonate. It decomposed to form 5.6 g of calcium oxide. The only other substance formed was carbon dioxide which was given off as a gas. What mass of carbon dioxide was formed?

4 Calculate the mass of copper(II) sulfate formed when 10 g of copper oxide reacts with excess sulfuric acid. The equation is:

$CuO + H_2SO_4 \longrightarrow CuSO_4 + H_2O$

5 Oliver reacted 56 g of iron powder with excess sulfuric acid. The predicted yield of iron(II) sulfate was 152 g. After crystallisation, Oliver obtained 136.8 g of iron(II) sulfate. Calculate the percentage yield.

6 Describe how you could prepare a pure dry sample of potassium nitrate using a titration method.

7 State the name of the acids and alkalis needed to prepare:

(a) ammonium nitrate

(b) ammonium phosphate.

8 Calculate the percentage of potassium in the fertiliser potassium nitrate KNO_3.

C4d Making ammonia & C4f Batch or continuous?

After revising these items you should:

- understand how ammonia is made by the Haber Process and the conditions used, give some uses of ammonia and understand about batch and continuous processes, speciality and bulk chemicals and development and production costs.

The Haber Process

Ammonia is produced in great quantities to make fertilisers. Fertilisers are put on the soil to increase crop growth so that enough food can be produced for the ever expanding world population.

Ammonia is made from nitrogen and hydrogen. The reaction is a **reversible reaction** – it can go in either direction.

N_2	+	$3H_2$	$\rightleftharpoons$	$2NH_3$	
nitrogen	+	hydrogen	$\rightleftharpoons$	ammonia	

The nitrogen comes from the air. The hydrogen comes from natural gas or the cracking of oil fractions.

Conditions used:

- high pressure
- temperature of 450°C
- the presence of an iron catalyst.

High pressure increases the percentage yield of ammonia because it pushes the hydrogen and nitrogen molecules together.

The increase in temperature has two effects:

- It increases the rate of reaction.
- It lowers the percentage yield of ammonia.

A 'compromise' temperature of 450°C is chosen to give a fast reaction with a sufficiently high yield of ammonia.

Some important points:

- Nitrogen and hydrogen combine in a reactor vessel packed with the iron catalyst.
- The iron catalyst increases the rate of reaction but does not change the percentage yield of ammonia.
- Not all the nitrogen and hydrogen combine to make ammonia.
- Unreacted nitrogen and hydrogen are recycled so they are not wasted.
- Ammonia is made all the time as more hydrogen and nitrogen go into the reactor, and is continuously removed as a liquid. This type of process is called a **continuous process**.

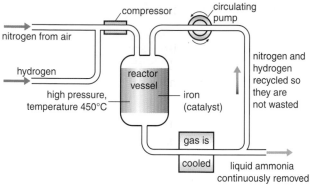

The Haber process.

Exam tip

You must be able to interpret data in tables or graphs which show percentage yields in reversible reactions.

The cost of making a substance

The total cost of making a product like ammonia depends on the cost of these factors:

gas or electricity which supplies the energy	higher temperature and pressure means greater energy cost
starting material	costs can be reduced by recycling unreacted materials
labour (wages)	using computer **automation** reduces costs as fewer workers are needed to operate the chemical process
chemical equipment (chemical plant)	carrying out the process under pressure needs special plant, which is expensive
catalysts	the rate of reaction must be high enough to give a good daily yield of product – catalysts help reduce the cost by speeding up the reaction

The conditions used in making a chemical must give the highest possible daily yield of product which is economical.

This means that the optimum (best) conditions are those which give the lowest cost (rather than the fastest reaction or the highest percentage yield). A low yield is acceptable if the reaction is repeated many times and the starting materials are recycled.

Making speciality chemicals

Chemicals such as medicines and **pharmaceutical drugs** are often made by a **batch process**. This means that they are made in small quantities as and when they are needed.

These speciality chemicals are made on a small scale compared with bulk chemicals such as ammonia which require a large-scale continuous process.

Exam tip

You must be prepared to answer questions comparing batch and continuous processes when given relevant data and information.

The raw materials for producing speciality chemicals are made:

- synthetically (from other laboratory chemicals), or
- from chemicals extracted from plants.

We can extract chemicals from plants by:

1 Crushing the plant.
2 Dissolving the crushed material in a suitable solvent.
3 Using **chromatography** to separate the required chemical.

The cost of developing a new substance

Development of a new medicine or pharmaceutical drug is expensive. The product may be on the market for many years before it pays for the cost of its own development. The spider diagram shows the costs involved.

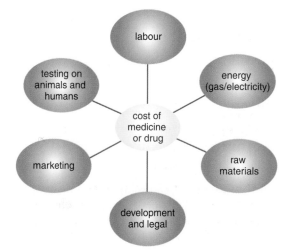

Test yourself

1 A rare acid is found in some trees in India. Only one company in the world supplies it. A standard bottle of this chemical contains 5 g. A scientist wants to use this acid for her research. Why is this acid so expensive for her to buy? Give at least two reasons.

2 Why are pharmaceutical drugs tested on animals before they are tested on human volunteers?

3 Explain why the synthesis of ammonia is not carried out:

(a) at temperatures much greater than 450°C
(b) at temperatures much less than 450°C.

4 The table shows the monthly demand in kilograms for two chemicals, A and B.

Month	Jan	Feb	Mar	Apr	May	Jun	Jul
A	500	50	1050	24	10	150	250
B	55 000	60 000	65 000	55 000	70 000	75 000	55 000

(a) What is the advantage of making chemical A by a batch process?
(b) What is the disadvantage of making chemical B by a batch process?

5 The table shows the yield of ammonia in the Haber Process when different pressures are used in the reaction vessel. The temperature is kept the same.

percentage yield (%)	12	22	38	50	55	59
pressure (atmospheres)	50	100	200	300	400	500

(a) Using this information estimate the percentage yield obtained when the pressure is 75 atmospheres and 600 atmospheres.
(b) The chief chemist suggests that the process is carried out at a pressure of no more than 200 atmospheres. What are his reasons for this?

C4e Detergents

What are detergents?

A **detergent** is a substance which cleans. Detergents include:

• washing powders
• washing-up liquids
• soaps.

Many detergents, especially soaps, are salts made by the neutralisation of acids with alkalis. Many synthetic detergents are made from chemicals in crude oil.

This simplified diagram of a detergent molecule shows that it has a charged end and an uncharged end.

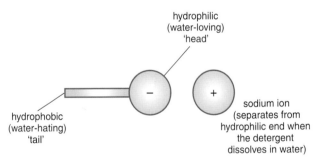

hydrophilic (water-loving) 'head'

hydrophobic (water-hating) 'tail'

sodium ion (separates from hydrophilic end when the detergent dissolves in water)

The charged 'head' end is water loving (hydrophilic), so it is attracted to water.

The uncharged 'tail' end is water hating (hydrophobic), so it is attracted to oil and grease.

How do detergents clean?

When clothes are washed:

1 The grease-loving 'tails' of the detergent molecules are attracted to the greasy dirt.

2 The detergent 'tails' stick into the grease.

3 The 'heads' are attracted to the water molecules.

4 The attraction between the 'heads' and the water molecules causes the grease to gradually roll up into a ball.

5 As this happens, the grease is pulled off the clothes.

6 The balls of grease are kept suspended in the water so that they do not go back onto the clothes.

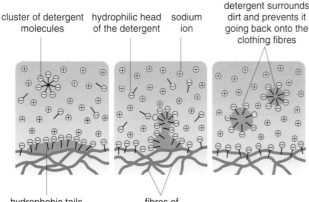

Exam tip

Make sure that you know the meaning of chemical terms such as solute, solution, solvent, soluble, insoluble, hydrophilic and hydrophobic.

The best way to wash clothes

The advantages of washing clothes at a low temperature with the correct powder are:

• less energy used

• less shrinkage caused

• less likely to damage clothes made from silk or wool.

Enzymes are biological catalysts used in low temperature washes to remove food stains. They do not work well at temperatures above 40°C.

Water molecules have small positive and negative charges. They attract and dissolve other substances which are charged. They do not attract molecules like grease molecules which have no charge.

Some clothes cannot be washed in water because they may shrink or they are dyed with colours which wash out easily. These clothes have to be dry-cleaned.

Dry-cleaning

The spider diagram shows why **dry-cleaning** is useful.

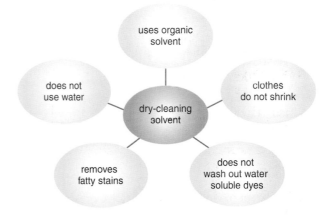

Dry-cleaning works like this:

1 There are intermolecular forces of attraction between the grease molecules and the dry-cleaning solvent molecules.

2 These forces make the grease molecules dissolve in the dry-cleaning solvent.

3 The solution of grease is removed leaving some solvent on the clothes. This solvent evaporates off the clothes.

4 The clothes are left clean.

Exam tip

In the exam you may be asked to comment on data from experiments which compare how well different washing powders and dry-cleaning solvents remove dirt and stains.

How science works

Juan wants to compare how well grease dissolves in four different solvents. The solvents all evaporate readily and some are poisonous.

Suggest how he could carry out the experiment to make it a fair test.

Test yourself

1 Gordon has a shirt that has been stained with food. He washes the shirt at 60°C with a washing powder containing enzymes. Not all the stain is removed. Why is this?

2 What are the advantages of washing clothes at a low temperature?

3 Five equally stained pieces of cotton were washed under different conditions. The results are shown in the table. Suggest reasons for the differences in stain removal.

Treatment	Soap at 30°C	Soap at 60°C	Enzyme washing powder at 30°C	Dry-cleaning solvent
Dirt removed (%)	45	55	75	90

4 Which of the following will dissolve grease?

   A Dry-cleaning solvent.
   B Water.
   C Salt solution.

   Give reasons for your answer.

5 State two advantages of dry-cleaning over cleaning with a detergent.

C4g Nanochemistry

After revising this item you should:

● be able to describe the three forms of carbon, their properties and uses and understand the concept of nanochemistry.

Diamond and graphite – structure and properties

Different forms of the same element are called **allotropes**. There are three allotropes of carbon:

● diamond
● graphite
● buckminsterfullerene

The diagrams shows the structures of the first two.

(a)
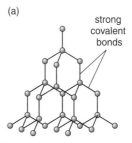
strong covalent bonds

(b)
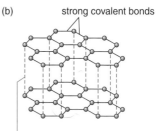
strong covalent bonds

weak bonds between layers

The arrangement of carbon atoms in (a) diamond (b) graphite.

Properties of graphite:

● black solid with a layered structure
● strong covalent bonding within the layers
● weak forces between the layers
● high melting point due to the presence of many strong covalent bonds which need to be broken
● slippery because the layers can slide over each other due to the weak forces between them.

Not all of the electrons in graphite are involved in bonding the carbon atoms covalently. Some are free to move along the layers.

These electrons are called **delocalised** electrons (see page 38). Graphite conducts electricity because these delocalised electrons can move when a voltage is applied.

Properties of diamond:

- lustrous, colourless solid
- very hard
- high melting point
- does not conduct electricity because it has no delocalised electrons to move.

The hardness and high melting point of diamond is due to the presence of many strong covalent bonds. These cannot be broken unless the temperature is extremely high.

Buckminsterfullerene

Buckminsterfullerene is a molecule which has 60 carbon atoms arranged like a football. Its formula is C_{60}.

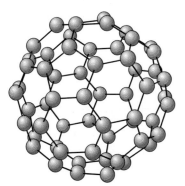

Fullerenes can be used as cages to trap other molecules. One idea is to trap drug molecules inside the cage or attach drugs to the outside of the cage and use the fullerenes to deliver drugs to where they are needed in the body. This means there will be less damage to other cells in the body.

Nanotubes

Fullerenes can be joined together to make **nanotubes**. The cylindrical shape of nanotubes makes them very strong. Like graphite, they conduct electricity.

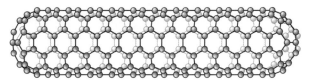

Nanotubes can be used as:
- semiconductors in electrical circuits
- industrial catalysts
- reinforcement for the graphite in tennis rackets.

When nanotubes are used as catalysts, groups of catalyst atoms are attached to the outer surface of the nanotube. A huge surface area is available for catalysis because they are so small.

Nanochemistry

Molecular manufacturing means making substances on a very small scale.

In recent years scientists have been able to move groups of atoms around on special surfaces and create materials, like nanotubes, at the atomic level. They build up the product a few atoms at a time, or atoms are removed from a larger structure a few at a time. We call this process of arranging atoms **positional chemistry**.

Chemists have found that **nanoparticles** have different properties from 'bulk' chemicals (chemicals used on a larger scale). Nanochemistry works on a very small scale compared to traditional chemistry, which uses 'bulk' chemicals on a large scale.

C4h How pure is our water?

After revising this item you should:

- be able to describe the chemicals which pollute our water, the processes used in water purification and some ways of testing for particular ions dissolved in water.

Water resources

In many developing nations clean water is a resource often in short supply. Lack of water destroys crops and kills animals. In these countries water may come from wells or ponds which are contaminated with microbes which cause disease.

Even in wetter countries it is important to conserve water because occasional droughts or overuse can lead to water shortages.

In some countries where there is little rain, seawater is distilled to make fresh water.

- This is expensive because it uses a lot of energy.
- The water produced has no taste because it has no dissolved salts.
- The water is free from contaminating materials.

How is water purified?

Before it is purified, water may contain:

- dissolved salts and minerals
- microbes
- insoluble materials such as animal remains and clay particles.

The diagram shows the stages in water purification.

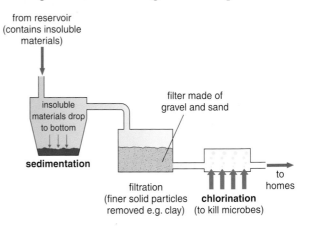

Water pollution

Pollutants are sometimes present in our purified water supply. They are difficult to remove during water purification because they are soluble in water.

They are generally present in such low concentrations that they are not harmful to health.

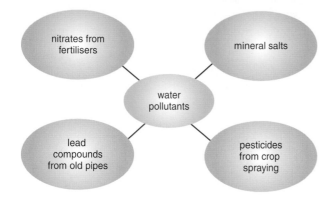

Some tests for ions

You can test for particular ions that may be present in water. These tests involve precipitation reactions (see page 38). You add a few drops of a colourless test solution to the water sample and observe the colour of the precipitate.

Ion tested for	Test solution added	Result if the ion is present
sulfate	barium chloride	white precipitate
chloride	silver nitrate	white precipitate
bromide	silver nitrate	cream precipitate
iodide	silver nitrate	pale yellow precipitate

Exam tip

You must remember the colours of the precipitates in these tests because you might be asked to interpret data about the testing of water.

The equation for the sulfate test is:

$$Na_2SO_4 + BaCl_2 \rightarrow BaSO_4 + 2NaCl$$
sodium sulfate + barium chloride → barium sulfate + sodium chloride
(white precipitate)

In this equation (and the one that follows) you can replace sodium with the name of another metal.

The word equations for the halide test all follow a similar pattern. Halides include:

- chlorides
- bromides
- iodides.

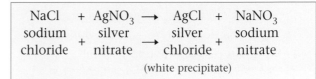

$$NaCl + AgNO_3 \rightarrow AgCl + NaNO_3$$
sodium chloride + silver nitrate → silver chloride + sodium nitrate
(white precipitate)

How science works

The table compares the amount of dissolved solids in the tap water in two towns. Nine samples were collected from different areas within each town.

Town	Amount of dissolved solids (mg/dm³)								
Addles	65.5	71.0	58.5	80.5	60.0	64.5	85.5	15.0	76.5
Becton	70	70	80	75	85	80	70	70	70

To what extent can these figures be used to compare the amount of dissolved solids in the two towns?

Test yourself

1 Explain why tap water is not pure water.

2 Drinking water often contains mineral salts which are not removed during water purification. Explain why this does not matter.

3 Why is it dangerous to drink unpurified water?

4 Write a symbol equation for the reaction of magnesium bromide solution with silver nitrate solution.

5 Anthea added a few drops of barium chloride solution to a sample of water. She observed that a white precipitate formed. Explain this observation with the aid of a symbol equation.

C5a Moles and empirical formulae

After revising this item you should:

- understand how to predict the amounts of reactants used, or products produced, in a reaction and be able to work out the formula of a compound.

Molar masses

The average relative atomic mass of an element is the average mass of an atom of an element compared with mass of 1/12 of an atom of carbon-12.

The relative **formula mass** in grams is calculated by adding together the relevant atomic masses in the Periodic Table. The relative formula mass in grams is called the **molar mass**.

element or compound	Br_2	SO_2	$Mg(NO_3)_2$
calculation	2×80	$32 + (2 \times 16)$	$24 + 2 \times [14 + (3 \times 16)]$
molar mass (g)	160	64	148

Reacting masses

In a chemical reaction, the total mass of the reactants is the same as the total mass of the products.

You can use simple maths to calculate the mass of product obtained from a given amount of reactant. For example:

When 24 g of magnesium react with 16 g of oxygen, 40 g of magnesium oxide is made. How many grams of magnesium oxide can be made from 6 g of magnesium?

24 g of magnesium gives 40 g of magnesium oxide so 6 g of magnesium gives $(6 \div 24) \times 40 = 10$ g magnesium oxide.

Moles

The scientific unit for amount of substance is the **mole**.

$$\text{number of moles} = \frac{\text{mass taken (in grams)}}{\text{molar mass (in grams)}}$$

If you weigh out the molar mass of a substance, you have a mole of that substance. For example:

- 40 g of bromine (Br_2) (molar mass: $2 \times 80 = 160$)
  = $40 \div 160$ moles
  = 0.25 moles of Br_2
- 880 g of CO_2 (molar mass: $12 + (2 \times 16) = 44$)
  = $880 \div 44$ moles
  = 20 moles of CO_2

Exam tip

Make sure you know how to rearrange this equation, so that you can calculate mass from number of moles (mass = molar mass × number of moles).

To find the mass of an element in a given number of moles of a compound:

1. Find the molar mass of that element in the compound.
2. Multiply it by the number of moles.

For example:

What mass of iron is present in 0.5 moles of iron(III) oxide (Fe_2O_3)? (Fe = 56)

molar mass of iron in $Fe_2O_3 = 2 \times 56 = 112$ (since there are two atoms of iron)

mass of iron = 112×0.5
= 56 g

Mole calculations

You can work out how much product is made from a given mass of reactant if you know the equation for the reaction.

1. Work out the molar masses.
2. Multiply them by the numbers in front of the formulae. These show the relative numbers of moles that react.

For example:

> Calculate the mass of water formed when 2g of methane (CH_4) is burned. (C = 12; H = 4; O = 16)
>
> $$CH_4 + 2O_2 \rightarrow CO_2 + 2H_2O$$
>
> | 1 mole methane | gives | 2 moles water |
> |---|---|---|
> | $12 + (4 \times 1)$ | | $2 \times (2 + 16)$ |
> | 16 g methane | gives | 36 g water |
> | So 2 g methane | gives | $\dfrac{2}{16} \times 36 = 4.5\,g$ water |

Exam tip

When doing calculations, only work out the molar masses that are relevant to the question. Identify the relevant substances and underline them in the equation.

How science works

Chromium is produced in a batch process by reacting a known amount of chromium(III) oxide with a calculated amount of aluminium powder.

Why is it important to know how much of each material to use?

Empirical formulae

The **empirical formula** gives the simplest whole number ratio of each type of atom in a compound.

The following diagram shows how to calculate the empirical formula of a compound.

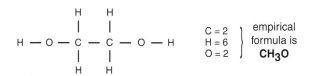

You can calculate the empirical formula by starting with:

- either the percentage composition by mass
- or the mass of each element in a sample of the compound.

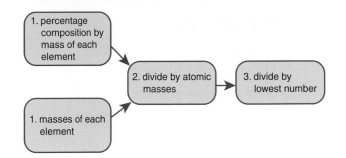

For example:

1. Calculate the empirical formula of a compound containing 38.70% carbon, 9.67% hydrogen and 51.60% oxygen.

   (H = 1; C = 12; O = 16)

	carbon	hydrogen	oxygen
percentage composition by mass	38.70	9.67	51.60
divide by atomic masses	38.7/12 = 3.225	9.67/1 = 9.67	51.6/16 – 3.225
divide by lowest number	3.225/3.225 = 1	9.67/3.225 = 3	3.225/3.225 = 1
empirical formula	CH_3O		

2. A compound contains 25.56 g of carbon, 4.26 g of hydrogen and 170.40 g of bromine. Calculate the empirical formula of this compound. (H = 1; C = 12; Br = 80)

	carbon	hydrogen	bromine
percentage composition by mass	25.56	4.26	170.40
divide by atomic masses	25.56/12 = 2.13	4.26/1 = 4.26	170.40/80 = 2.13
divide by lowest number	2.13/2.13 = 1	4.26/2.13 = 2	2.13/2.13 = 1
empirical formula	CH_2Br		

Exam tip

When doing calculations always show your working. It helps to put the relevant numbers below each compound in the equation, so you can see clearly which figures to use.

Relative atomic masses Al = 27; Fe = 56; H = 1; I = 127; Mg = 24; N = 14; Na = 23; O = 16; S = 32)

1 Calculate the molar mass of:

(a) $MgSO_4$ (b) Fe_3O_4 (c) $(NH_4)_2SO_4$

2 Calculate the mass (in grams) of:

(a) 0.5 moles of sodium sulfate (Na_2SO_4)
(b) 6 moles of aluminium oxide (Al_2O_3)
(c) 0.2 moles of iodine (I_2).

3 Calculate the number of moles in:

(a) 6 g of magnesium
(b) 22.4 g of iron oxide (Fe_2O_3)
(c) 160 g of sodium hydroxide (NaOH).

4 Calculate the mass of magnesium oxide formed when 3.0 g of magnesium reacts with excess oxygen.

5 What is the empirical formula of a compound of nitrogen and oxygen containing 4.2 g of nitrogen and 9.6 g of oxygen?

C5b Electrolysis

After revising this item you should:

- be able to describe and write equations for the electrolysis of molten and aqueous salts and explain the mass changes at the electrodes when copper(II) sulfate solution is electrolysed.

Electrolysis

Electrolysis is the decomposition of a liquid, called an electolyte, by passing electric current through it.

The next diagram shows a simple electrolysis cell.

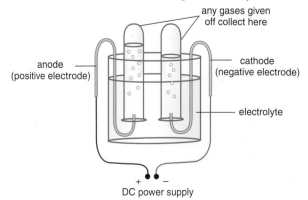

During electrolysis:

- moving ions transfer charge in the electrolyte
- electrons transfer the charge in the wires.

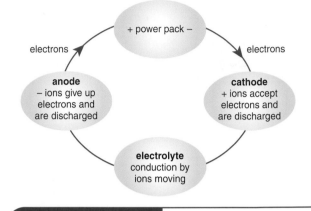

In Canada, large concrete electrolysis cells are built around boulders to extract the copper from them. This happens in remote, scenic areas with little population.

What social, economic and environmental problems might arise from this?

Decomposing molten electrolytes

Ionic substances can be electrolysed only when they are molten or in solution.

- When solid the ions are in fixed positions and cannot move.
- When the solid is melted (or dissolved) the ions can move and conduct electricity.

The products of electrolysis of a molten salt are a metal and a non-metal.

For example, when lead(II) bromide is electrolysed, lead and bromine are discharged (formed) at the electrodes.

We can write half equations to show what happens at the electrodes:

- positive ions move to the **negative electrode** (cathode) and accept electrons.

$$Pb^{2+} + 2e^- \longrightarrow Pb$$
$$Al^{3+} + 3e^- \longrightarrow Al$$

- negative ions move to the **positive electrode** (anode) where they give up electrons.

$$2Br^- - 2e^- \longrightarrow Br_2$$
$$2O^{2-} - 4e^- \longrightarrow O_2$$

Exam tip

When writing half equations you will be given the formulae of the ions in the electrolyte.

- *Metal ions (and hydrogen) are positive.*
- *Non-metal ions are negative.*
- *Electrons gained at the negative electrode are shown on the left of the arrow and electrons lost from the positive electrode are shown on the right.*

Electrolysing dilute solutions

When dilute solutions such as potassium sulfate or potassium nitrate in water are electrolysed, hydrogen is discharged at the cathode (–) and oxygen at the anode (+).

This is because it is easier to discharge these gases from the H^+ and OH^- ions in water than to discharge the metal, sulfate or nitrate ions.

The half equations for these reactions are:

- at the anode: $4OH^- - 4e^- \longrightarrow O_2 + 2H_2O$
- at the cathode: $2H^+ + 2e^- \longrightarrow H_2$

Electrolysing copper(II) sulfate solution

When copper(II) sulfate solution is electrolysed with copper electrodes, both electrodes change in mass.

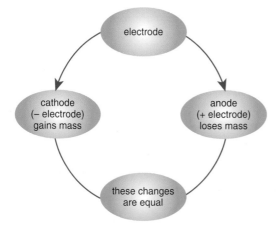

The half equations are:

- at the anode: $Cu - 2e^- \longrightarrow Cu^{2+}$
- at the cathode: $Cu^{2+} + 2e^- \longrightarrow Cu$

When copper sulfate solution is electrolysed with inert electrodes (e.g. graphite), oxygen is produced at the anode and copper is deposited at the

cathode. The solution of copper sulfate gradually decolourises as the copper ions are discharged.

How science works

Ermelinda investigates the amount of copper deposited at the negative electrode when copper sulfate solution is electrolysed. She does the experiment several times using the same copper electrode.

The table shows her results. Comment on the reliability and validity of these results.

	1st run	2nd run	3rd run	4th run	5th run	6th run
mass of electrode at start (g)	14.00	14.50	15.05	15.75	16.25	16.80
mass of electrode at end (g)	14.50	15.05	15.75	16.25	16.80	17.30

Current, time and copper deposition

When copper(II) sulfate solution is electrolysed, the amount of copper deposited on the cathode (or removed from the anode) increases proportionally with both time and current.

- The time (t) in seconds multiplied by the current (I) in amperes is called the charge (Q).
- The amount of copper deposited is proportional to the charge.
- Charge is measured in coulombs.

$$
\begin{array}{ccccc}
Q & = & I & \times & t \\
\text{charge} & = & \text{current} & \times & \text{time} \\
\text{(coulombs)} & & \text{(amps)} & & \text{(seconds)}
\end{array}
$$

Exam tip

When calculating charge, do not forget to change minutes to seconds by multiplying by 60.

For example:

When molten lead(II) iodide is electrolysed using a current of 12 A for 50 minutes, approximately 39 g of lead is deposited. What mass of lead is produced using a current of 6 A for 25 minutes?

Using $Q = I \times t$

- for 12 A and 50 min, the charge is
  $Q = 12 \times 50 \times 60 = 36\,000$ coulombs
- for 6 A and 25 min, the charge is
  $Q = 6 \times 25 \times 60 = 9\,000$ coulombs
- 36 000 coulombs deposits 39 g of lead
- so 9000 coulombs deposits
  $39 \times \dfrac{9000}{36\,000} = 9.75\,g$

Test yourself

1 What substances are formed at the positive and negative electrodes when these molten salts are electrolysed?

   (a) lead(II) iodide   (b) potassium chloride
   (c) aluminium oxide.

2 Name the substances produced at the positive and negative electrodes when a dilute solution of sodium nitrate is electrolysed.

3 A copper(II) sulfate solution is electrolysed. The cathode increases in mass by 0.5 g. What happens to the mass of the anode? (The electrodes are made of copper.)

4 Write half equations for the electrode processes occurring at each electrode when these molten compounds are electrolysed. (Formulae for ions: Al^{3+}; Br^-; Cl^-; I^-; K^+; O^{2-}; Pb^{2+})

   (a) KCl   (b) Al_2O_3
   (c) $PbBr_2$ (d) PbI_2

5 When molten lead(II) iodide is electrolysed it requires a charge of 920 coulombs to deposit 1 g of lead. What mass of lead is produced using a current of 11.5 A for 8 minutes?

C5c Quantitative analysis & C5d Titrations

After revising these items you should:

- be able to measure solution concentration, understand about recommended daily allowances (RDA) of foods, how indicators are used in acid/alkali titrations and how we use titrations to calculate the concentrations of acids or alkalis.

Calculating concentrations

Concentration is the amount of substance in a given volume of the solution. The more concentrated a solution, the more crowded the solute particles.

$$\text{concentration} = \frac{\text{moles}}{\text{volume (dm}^3\text{)}}$$

Concentration is measured in grams per decimetre cubed (g/dm^3) or moles per decimetre cubed (mol/dm^3).

You need to know the conversions in this table.

Conversion required	What you have to do	Example
volume: cm^3 to dm^3	divide by 1000	$150\,cm^3 = 150 \div 1000$ $= 0.15\,dm^3$
volume: dm^3 to cm^3	multiply by 1000	$0.035\,dm^3 = 0.035 \times 1000$ $= 35\,cm^3$
concentration: g/dm^3 to mol/dm^3	divide by molar mass	$30\,g/dm^3$ $MgSO_4$ (molar mass 120) $30 \div 120 = 0.25\,mol/dm^3$
concentration: mol/dm^3 to g/dm^3	multiply by molar mass	$0.5\,mol/dm^3$ KBr (molar mass 119) $0.5 \times 119 = 59.5\,g/dm^3$

Exam tip

Whenever doing calculations involving volumes, be clear whether you are working in centimetres cubed (cm^3) or decimetres cubed (dm^3) and that $1\,dm^3 = 1000\,cm^3$.

You also need to know how to rearrange the equation for calculating concentration. Volumes are in decimetres cubed (dm^3).

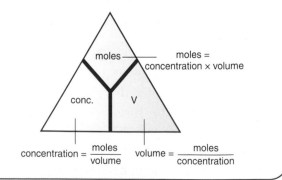

moles = concentration × volume

$$\text{concentration} = \frac{\text{moles}}{\text{volume}} \qquad \text{volume} = \frac{\text{moles}}{\text{concentration}}$$

Diluting solutions

The next diagram shows you how to dilute a $1 \, mol/dm^3$ solution to make a $0.1 \, mol/dm^3$ solution. The **dilution** needed is $1 \div 0.1 = 10 \times$ dilution.

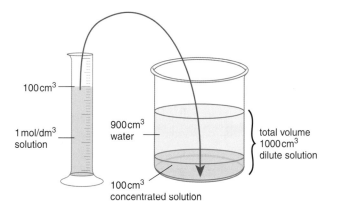

Exam tip

- *When making a 10× dilution, add one part concentrated solution and nine parts water.*
- *When making a 5× dilution add one part concentrated solution and four parts water.*

Recommended daily allowances

Excess **salt** is bad for us. The Recommended Daily Allowances (RDAs) on food labels tell us the maximum amount of salt or other substances allowed per day if we are to keep healthy.

RDAs usually give the amount of sodium rather than the amount of salt (**sodium chloride**), so always interpret these figures with care. Also, the raw food material may contain salt or other ions which are not accounted for on the label.

You can find the amount of sodium chloride (NaCl) from the sodium content by using moles. For example:

If the RDA is 3 g of sodium, the amount of salt can be found as follows. ($Na = 23$; $Cl = 35.5$)
- moles of sodium = $3 \div 23 = 0.13$ moles = moles of sodium chloride (NaCl)
- mass = moles × molar mass
- so 0.13 moles of sodium chloride = $0.13 \times (23 + 35.5) = 7.6 \, g$.

How pH changes during titrations

The next graph shows how pH changes when an alkali is added to an acid (see also C4a Acids and bases, page 40). You should be able to sketch this **titration** curve.

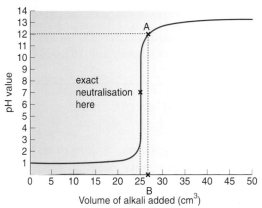

- The neutralisation point of the titration is $25 \, cm^3$.
- To calculate the volume of alkali added when the pH is 12, read across to point A then draw a line down to point B.

The pH changes because of the neutralisation reaction.

acid	+	alkali	→	salt	+	water
(low pH)		(high pH)		(neutral pH)		

Exam tip

You should also be able to draw a titration curve for an acid being added to an alkali. In this case the curve starts at a high pH, e.g. pH 12, and finishes at a low pH, e.g pH 2.

Titrations and indicators

In acid–alkali titrations it is important to get consistent readings. You need several titres that are not more than $0.2 \, cm^3$ apart. A titre is the volume of acid added to neutralise an alkali (or the volume of alkali needed to neutralise an acid).

At the end point of a titration, the indicator should change colour suddenly.

- Only **single indicators**, such as methyl orange, change colour suddenly.
- **Mixed indicators** such as **universal indicator** cannot be used to find the end point because they produce a gradual colour change near this point.

Richard titrated some ammonia with $0.1\,mol/dm^3$ hydrochloric acid. The table shows his results.

	1st run	2nd run	3rd run	4th run	5th run
titre/cm³	15.5	15.8	15.35	15	15.5

Comment on the consistency and accuracy of these results.

Calculating acid or alkali concentrations

You can calculate the concentration of an acid or alkali from titration results. For example:

$24\,cm^3$ of a solution of sodium hydroxide (NaOH) of concentration $0.1\,mol/dm^3$ was required to exactly neutralise $16\,cm^3$ of hydrochloric acid (HCl). Calculate the concentration of the hydrochloric acid.

$$NaOH + HCl \longrightarrow NaCl + H_2O$$

Step 1: Find the number of moles of sodium hydroxide (divide volume by 1000 to convert it to decimetres cubed (dm³)).

moles = concentration × volume

$$\frac{24}{1000} \times 0.1 = 2.4 \times 10^{-3} \text{ moles NaOH}$$

In the calculations for your exam, the number of moles of H^+ ions in the equation equals the number of moles of OH^- ions.

So moles of hydrochloric acid = 2.4×10^{-3} moles.

Step 2: Find the concentration of hydrochloric acid (divide volume by 1000 to convert it to decimetres cubed (dm³)).

$$\text{concentration} = \frac{\text{moles}}{\text{volume (dm}^3)}$$

$$\frac{2.4 \times 10^{-3}}{16 \div 1000} = 0.15\,mol/dm^3$$

Exam tip

For step 1, identify the acid or alkali for which you have both concentration and volume and make sure that you use the correct volume.

Test yourself

1 Sketch a graph to show the pH changes when an alkali is added to an acid.

2 Convert the following to moles per decimetre cubed (mol/dm³).

   (a) $11.2\,g$ copper(II) bromide ($CuBr_2$) in $1\,dm^3$.
   (b) $30\,g$ sodium hydroxide (NaOH) in $1\,dm^3$.

3 Convert the following to grams per decimetre cubed (g/dm³).

   (a) $0.5\,mol/dm^3$ sodium hydroxide (NaOH).
   (b) $1.5\,mol/dm^3$ sodium nitrate ($NaNO_3$).

4 According to the label, a tube of tomato paste contains tomatoes, yeast and herbs. It also contains $0.4\,g$ of added sodium. The sodium is present as salt (sodium chloride (NaCl)). Explain why the amount of sodium on the label may not be an accurate indication of the amount of salt in the tomato paste.

5 $80\,cm^3$ of sodium hydroxide solution neutralises $20\,cm^3$ of $0.4\,mol/dm^3$ hydrochloric acid. Calculate the concentration of the sodium hydroxide solution.

C5e Gas volumes

After revising this item you should:

● be able to describe how to measure and calculate volumes of gases involved in a reaction.

Measuring gas volumes

The volumes of gases produced during a reaction can be measured using:

• a gas syringe
• an upturned measuring cylinder filled with water, or
• an upturned burette filled with water.

Change of mass and gas volumes

In the reaction

$$CaCO_3 + 2HCl \longrightarrow CaCl_2 + CO_2 + H_2O$$

the mass of the reaction mixture decreases if carbon dioxide gas is allowed to escape.

Change in mass may be used to monitor the amount of gas produced:

1. Put the acid in a flask placed on a top pan balance.
2. Add the calcium carbonate and record the mass of the flask and reactants.
3. Record the mass at specific times (t) until the reaction stops.
   - (initial mass) – (mass at time t) is proportional to the volume of gas produced.

How the volume of gas changes

The following diagram shows how the volume of gas produced in a reaction changes with time.

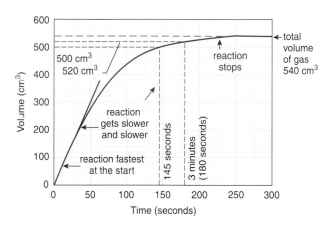

From this graph, you can find out:

- the time taken to produce a given volume of gas
- the volume of gas produced in a given time.

The curve of this graph shows:

- it takes 180 seconds to get 520 cm³ of gas
- the volume of gas produced in 145 seconds is 500 cm³.

Limiting reactants

A reaction stops when one of the reactants is completely used up.

- The reactant used up first is called the **limiting reactant**.
- The reactant that is not limiting is the reactant in excess.

The next diagram, for the reaction between calcium carbonate and hydrochloric acid (to form carbon dioxide), shows the course of the reaction when hydrochloric acid is limiting.

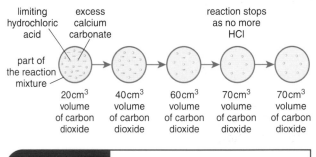

The total amount of gas produced is directly proportional to the amount of limiting reactant present.

The following graph shows how the volume of gas varies when excess hydrochloric acid reacts with limiting calcium carbonate.

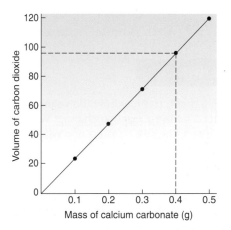

You can work out the volume of gas produced with different amounts of limiting reactant from a graph like this or by simple proportion. For example:

> If 2 g of calcium carbonate produces 480 cm³ of carbon dioxide, then 8 g of calcium carbonate produces $\frac{8}{2} \times 480 = 1920 \, cm^3$.

The volume of a mole of gas

One mole of any gas has a volume of 24 dm³ at room temperature and pressure.

> volume (dm³) = number of moles × 24

Use this equation to do calculations involving gas volumes and number of moles.

Exam tip

In calculations, if the volume is in centimetres cubed (cm³) you have to divide by 1000 to get decimetres cubed (dm³).

For example:

1. What is the volume of 0.25 moles of oxygen?
   volume (dm³) = moles × 24
   0.25 × 24 = 6 dm³

2. How many moles of hydrogen are there in 480 cm³ of hydrogen?

   480 cm³ = 0.48 dm³
   moles = volume (dm³) ÷ 24
         = 0.48 ÷ 24
         = 0.02 moles hydrogen

Test yourself

1 Sketch a graph to show how the volume of gas produced during a reaction changes with time. Show where the rate is fastest and where the reaction stops.

2 Zinc reacts with sulfuric acid to form hydrogen.
Zn + H_2SO_4 ⟶ $ZnSO_4$ + H_2
When 10 g of zinc reacts with 0.1 moles of sulfuric acid, which is the limiting reactant? (Zn = 65)

3 The table shows the total volume of hydrogen given off when different amounts of magnesium react with 100 cm³ of 1.0 mol/dm³ sulfuric acid. (Mg = 24)

Mass of magnesium (g)	Volume of hydrogen (cm³)
0.12 g	240 cm³
0.48 g	960 cm³
0.96 g	1920 cm³
1.2 g	2400 cm³
2 g	4000 cm³

Which is the limiting reactant when:

(a) 0.48 g of magnesium are used
(b) 2 g of magnesium are used?

4 Calculate the mass of carbon dioxide present in 600 cm³ of carbon dioxide gas at room temperature and pressure. (C = 12; O =16)

5 Calculate the volume of 200 g of sulfur dioxide gas at room temperature and pressure. (S = 32; O =16)

C5f Equilibria

After revising this item you should:

- understand about chemical equilibrium, why this is important in industry and how chemists alter reaction conditions in order to change the position of equilibrium.

Reversible reactions

In **reversible reactions**:

- the products can be changed back to the reactants by reversing the conditions
- the symbol ⇌ is used to show that a reaction is reversible.

Equilibrium

When the **forward** and **backward reactions** in a reversible reaction proceed at the same rate in a closed system, the reaction is in **equilibrium**.

The following spider diagram shows the features of equilibrium reactions.

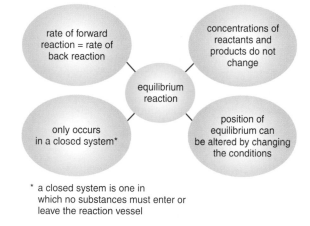

* a closed system is one in which no substances must enter or leave the reaction vessel

- If blue copper(II) sulfate crystals are heated in a test tube all the water escapes. So it is not a closed system, although the reaction is reversible.

- If the copper sulfate is heated in a closed vessel, both white and blue copper sulfate as well as water will be present in equilibrium.

The next diagram shows how equilibrium is reached.

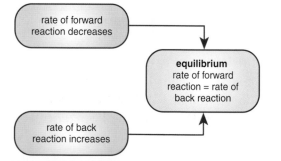

How science works

The blood pigment haemoglobin reacts with oxygen in an equilibrium reaction.

Scientists have been trying to make artificial haemoglobin from crocodile haemoglobin. The equilibrium in crocodile haemoglobin is shifted so that more oxygen is carried. They hope to use this artificial blood to help people who have breathing difficulties.

Suggest why this worries some people.

The position of equilibrium

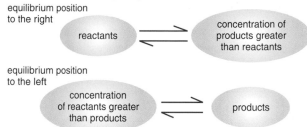

The effect of concentration and pressure

Changing the concentration of reactants or products changes the position of equilibrium.

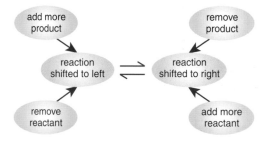

Increasing pressure moves the equilibrium to the side with the least number of moles of gas molecules. For example:

In the reaction

$$N_2(g) + 3H_2(g) \rightleftharpoons 2NH_3(g)$$

there are 4 moles of gas on the left and 2 on the right, so the equilibrium is shifted to the right.

Exam tip

If conditions change, the position of equilibrium will shift to minimise the change.

You may be asked to interpret data about equilibrium. For example:

This table shows the effect of pressure on the yield of ammonia produced in the Haber Process at a temperature of 350°C.

percentage yield of ammonia	35	54	65	70
pressure (atm)	100	200	300	400

You can see from this data that as pressure increases yield increases, so the position of equilibrium is shifted more to the right.

The Contact Process for making sulfuric acid

The following flow diagram shows the manufacture of sulfuric acid by the Contact Process.

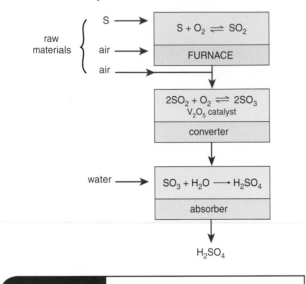

The next table explains some conditions used in the converter.

Condition	Explanation
vanadium (V) oxide (V_2O_5), catalyst	increases the rate of reaction but does not change the position of the equilibrium in the converter
high temperature, 450°C	decreases the yield of SO_3 but increases the rate of reaction
	it is the optimum (compromise) temperature
atmospheric pressure	the position of equilibrium is already to the right
	high pressure is expensive so not needed

How science works

In vehicle engines, nitrogen reacts with oxygen in an reversible reaction to produce nitrogen(II) oxide. Despite the use of catalytic converters some nitrogen(II) oxide still gets into the atmosphere where it may contribute to a smog of irritant chemicals.

What further steps could we take to reduce the amount of nitrogen(II) oxide in the atmosphere?

Test yourself

1 State three features of equilibrium reactions.

2 The equation for the reaction between carbon dioxide and hydrogen is
$$CO_2(g) + H_2(g) \rightleftharpoons H_2O(g) + CO(g)$$
How do:

(a)   adding steam, and
(b)   decreasing the pressure affect the reaction?

3 When calcium carbonate is heated in a closed container the following equilibrium is achieved:
$$CaCO_3 \rightleftharpoons CaO + CO_2$$
Explain why this equilibrium is reached.

4 Write word and symbol equations for the three reactions in the Contact Process.

5 The table shows the effect of temperature on the yield of ammonia produced by the equilibrium reaction in the Haber Process at constant pressure.

Percentage yield of ammonia	65	50	36	20
Temperature (°C)	350	400	450	500

What effect does temperature have on this equilibrium?

C5g Strong and weak acids & C5h Ionic equations

After revising these items you should:

● understand the difference between strong and weak acids in terms of degree of ionisation and know how to describe precipitation reactions and construct ionic equations.

Strong and weak acids

All acids ionise in water to produce hydrogen (H^+) ions. Acids can be strong or weak.

● **Strong acids** ionise completely in water to form ions. No molecules are present, e.g. hydrochloric acid:
$$HCl \longrightarrow H^+ + Cl^-$$

● **Weak acids** only ionise slightly in water to produce an equilibrium mixture containing acid molecules as well as ions.

The ionisation of a weak acid is an example of a reversible reaction, e.g. ethanoic acid:

$$CH_3CO_2H \rightleftharpoons CH_3CO_2^- + H^+$$

If we take the same concentration (in mol/dm^3) of weak and strong acids, the weak acid will have a lower concentration of hydrogen ions than the strong acid.

Electrolysing acids

Hydrogen gas is produced at the negative electrode when any acid is electrolysed.

This is because the positive hydrogen ions are attracted to this electrode where they are discharged as hydrogen.

$$2H^+ + 2e^- \longrightarrow H_2$$

Concentrated or dilute?

The same amounts of ethanoic acid (weak acid) and hydrochloric acid (strong acid) produce the same amounts of hydrogen gas when they react with magnesium.

They also produce the same amounts of carbon dioxide when they react with calcium carbonate. This is because all the hydrogen in the acid is used when they react.

- The total volume of gas formed depends on the amount of acid present (in moles), not the strength of the acid.

A dilute acid has a low concentration of acid particles compared with a concentrated acid.

- So $0.001 \, mol/dm^3$ hydrochloric acid is a dilute solution of a strong acid and $6 \, mol/dm^3$ ethanoic acid is a concentrated solution of a weak acid.

Comparing strong and weak acids

The following diagram compares some properties of strong and weak acids of the same concentration.

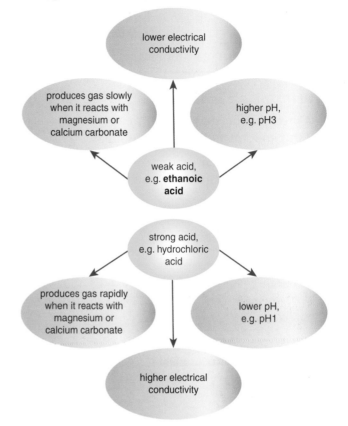

These differences are due a lower concentration of H^+ ions in weak acids than in strong acids.

Difference	Explanation
lower pH of weak acids	the higher the H^+ ion concentration, the lower the pH, so weak acids, with a lower concentration of H^+ ions, have a higher pH
slower rate of reaction of weak acid with magnesium	the lower concentration of H^+ ions in a weak acid means that collisions between acid and magnesium are less frequent than for a strong acid
lower electrical **conductivity** of weak acids	there are fewer H^+ ions available to move and carry charge compared with a strong acid

Uses of weak acids

Weak acids are used as limescale removers (**descalers**) because they have a gentle action. Strong acids are not used because they may damage the surface under the limescale.

Precipitation reactions

In a precipitation reaction two solutions react together to form an insoluble precipitate.

The following diagram shows some important points about a precipitation reaction.

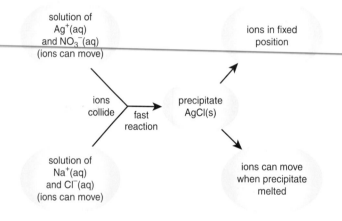

Preparing an insoluble salt

Insoluble salts can be prepared by precipitation reactions.

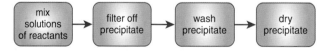

Ionic equations

The tests for sulfates and halides such as chlorides are precipitation reactions.

$$Na_2SO_4(aq) + BaCl_2(aq) \longrightarrow 2NaCl(aq) + BaSO_4(s)$$

sodium sulfate + barium chloride $\longrightarrow$ sodium chloride + barium sulfate

Exam tip

When revising, it is useful to know the tests for ions in C3g Transition elements (page 37) and C4h How pure is our water? (page 50).

You can convert a symbol equation into an **ionic equation** like this:

1 Write down the balanced equation (see earlier).

2 Write down the ions present in each compound, but not those in the precipitate.

$$2Na^+ + SO_4^{2-} + Ba^{2+} + 2Cl^- \longrightarrow 2Na^+ + 2Cl^- + BaSO_4$$

3 Cross out the ions which are the same on both sides. These are called the **spectator ions**. They play no part in the reaction.

$$2\overline{Na^+} + SO_4^{2-} + Ba^{2+} + 2\overline{Cl^-} \longrightarrow 2\overline{Na^+} + 2\overline{Cl^-} + BaSO_4$$

So the ionic equation including state symbols is

$$Ba^{2+}(aq) + SO_4^{2-}(aq) \longrightarrow BaSO_4(s)$$

Exam tip

When converting a symbol equation to an ionic equation, separate out the ions in the soluble substances (those with aq as a state symbol) but not those in the precipitate.

An easier way is to just include the ions that go to make the precipitate.

Test yourself

1 Write symbol equations for the ionisation of ethanoic acid and hydrochloric acid in water.

2 Hydrochloric acid and ethanoic acid both at a concentration of $1\,mol/dm^3$ react with magnesium, but the rate of reaction differs. Describe how and explain why the rate of reaction differs.

3 A $4\,mol/dm^3$ solution of ethanoic acid is a concentrated solution of a weak acid. Use ideas about particles to explain the difference between strength and concentration of an acid.

4 Silver nitrate solution reacts with potassium bromide solution to form a precipitate of silver bromide. Write an ionic equation for this reaction, including state symbols. (Formulae of ions: silver, Ag^+; bromide, Br^-)

5 Iron(II) chloride ($FeCl_2$) solution reacts with sodium hydroxide (NaOH) solution to form a precipitate of iron(II) hydroxide ($Fe(OH)_2$). Write the simplest ionic equation for this reaction. (Formulae of ions: iron(II), Fe^{2+}; chloride, Cl^-; sodium, Na^+; hydroxide, OH^-)

C6a Energy transfers – fuel cells

After revising this item you should:

- understand how fuel cells can be used to produce electricity.

Exothermic reactions

Hydrogen reacts with oxygen to make water. This is an exothermic reaction – it gives out heat to the surroundings.

Where does this heat energy come from? Look at this **energy level diagram** for the combustion of hydrogen.

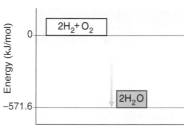

- The energy level of hydrogen and oxygen is higher than the energy level of water.
- The difference is 571.6 kJ.
- This amount of energy is given out into the surroundings as the hydrogen and oxygen react.

Fuel cells

1 A **fuel cell** is supplied with fuel, such as hydrogen and oxygen.

2 As the fuel and oxygen react, the energy from the reaction is used to create a **potential difference**. This can be used to drive an electric current round a circuit.

The following diagram shows a fuel cell using hydrogen as the fuel.

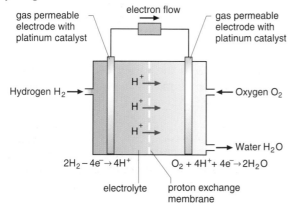

The overall reaction in this fuel cell is:

hydrogen + oxygen $\longrightarrow$ water

The electrode reactions are summarised here.

- At the negative electrode hydrogen gas is bubbled into the solution. Hydrogen releases electrons to form hydrogen ions (protons).

$$2H_2 - 4e^- \longrightarrow 4H^+$$

Hydrogen ions move across the fuel cell through the electrolyte to the positive electrode.

- At the positive electrode oxygen gas is bubbled into the solution. Oxygen combines with hydrogen ions and electrons to form water.

$$O_2 + 4H^+ + 4e^- \longrightarrow 2H_2O$$

This is a redox reaction:

- The oxygen gains electrons, and so is reduced.
- The hydrogen loses electrons, and so is oxidised.

Combining the two electrode reactions gives the overall equation for the reaction:

$$2H_2 + O_2 \longrightarrow 2H_2O$$

Exam tip

You need to be able to write equations for the reactions that take place at each electrode, and explain how they combine into the overall equation.

How science works

Hydrogen is an explosive gas. To store it effectively it has to be kept liquid at a temperature below −253°C. Using hydrogen in fuel cells poses a risk.

Explain why the benefits of using hydrogen in fuel cells outweigh the risks.

Advantage of fuel cells

Fuel cells are used to provide electricity in spacecraft because they:

- are light
- do not get very hot
- do not produce dangerous waste products.

The car industry is developing fuel cells.

- They provide far more energy per kilogram of mass than conventional lead–acid batteries.
- Unlike petrol engines, they produce no pollutant gases.
- Fuel cells will probably power the next generation of electric cars.

The following spider diagram shows some of the advantages fuel cells offer over conventional methods of generating electricity.

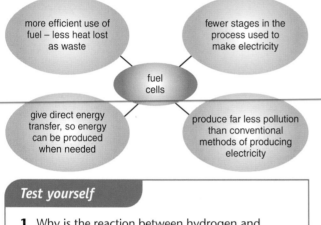

Test yourself

1 Why is the reaction between hydrogen and oxygen exothermic? Use ideas about bond making and bond breaking.

2 Explain how the reaction between hydrogen and oxygen is a redox reaction.

3 Hydrogen ions are produced in the fuel cell. What happens to them?

4 Why is a fuel cell a good source of electricity for a spacecraft?

5 Explain two advantages that the fuel cell has over conventional methods of electricity generation.

C6b Redox reactions

After revising this item you should:

- be able to use ideas of redox to explain reactions involving oxidation and reduction.

Rusting

The rusting of iron involves both oxygen and water.

iron + oxygen + water $\longrightarrow$ hydrated iron(III) oxide

In this reaction iron loses electrons and oxygen gains electrons – rusting is a redox reaction.

Preventing rust

The following table gives details of some methods used to prevent iron rusting.

Method of rust prevention	Description	Explanation
painting	surface is painted	the layer of paint, oil or grease on the iron keeps water and oxygen away from the iron
covering with oil or grease	surface is wiped with oil or grease	
tinning	the surface is covered with a thin layer of tin	the layer of tin on the iron keeps water and oxygen away from the iron, but if this layer is scratched the iron loses electrons in preference to the tin and so rusts even quicker
galvanising	surface is covered with a thin layer of zinc	the layer of zinc keeps water and oxygen away from the iron if this layer is scratched the zinc loses electrons in preference to the iron, still protecting it from rusting
sacrificial protection	a piece of a more reactive metal (e.g. magnesium) is attached to the iron	magnesium attached to the iron loses electrons in preference to the iron, protecting it from rusting

Displacement reactions of metals

When an iron nail is dipped into a solution of copper(II) sulfate for a few seconds, it becomes covered with a brown layer of copper.

Iron is more reactive than copper, and has displaced some of the copper(II) ions from the solution.

iron + copper(II) sulfate $\longrightarrow$ copper + iron(II) sulfate

- Iron atoms become iron(II) ions in the solution.
- Copper(II) ions in the solution become copper atoms on the outside of the iron nail.

$Fe + Cu^{2+} \longrightarrow Cu + Fe^{2+}$

The diagram shows common metals in order of their reactivity. A metal higher in this list will displace a metal lower in the list from its solution.

K
Na
Mg
Zn
Fe
Sn
Pb
Cu
Ag
Au

Redox reactions

A **redox reaction** involves both oxidation and reduction.

Iron reacts with chlorine to produce iron(III) chloride.

$$2Fe + 3Cl_2 \longrightarrow 2FeCl_3$$

The ionic equation for this redox reaction is:

$$2Fe + 3Cl_2 \longrightarrow 2Fe^{3+} + 6Cl^-$$

In this reaction the iron atoms lose electrons.

$$Fe - 3e^- \longrightarrow Fe^{3+}$$

- Loss of electrons is oxidation, so the iron has been oxidised.

Chlorine atoms gain electrons.

$$Cl_2 + 2e^- \longrightarrow 2Cl^-$$

- Gain of electrons is reduction, so the chlorine has been reduced.

How science works

When magnesium metal is added to hydrochloric acid (which contains H^+ ions), hydrogen gas is displaced from the acid.

Use ideas about redox to develop a model to explain this observation.

Oxidising agents and reducing agents

In the redox reaction between iron and chlorine:

$$Fe + Cl_2 \longrightarrow Fe^{2+} + 2Cl^-$$

- as chlorine is itself reduced, it oxidises the iron – chlorine is an **oxidising agent**
- as iron is itself oxidised, it reduces the chlorine – iron is a **reducing agent**.

If iron(II) ions are reacted with a more powerful reducing agent, such as hydrogen, they can be reduced to iron atoms.

$$Fe^{2+} + 2e^- \longrightarrow Fe$$

Several types of systems can undergo either reduction or oxidation, depending on the substance they react with, as shown in this table.

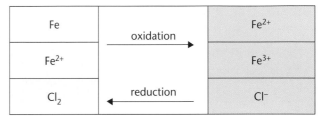

Test yourself

1 Iron will not rust if exposed to dry oxygen. Suggest why.

2 Why does galvanising give iron better protection from rusting than tinning?

3 Ross drops a piece of magnesium into a solution of iron(II) sulfate. Describe and explain what he will see.

4 Use an example to explain what is meant by an oxidising agent.

5 Use ideas about redox to explain what is happening in this reaction.
$$Sn + Pb(NO_3)_2 \longrightarrow Pb + Sn(NO_3)_2$$

6 When zinc is added to a solution of copper(II) sulfate it displaces copper from the solution. Write an overall equation and ionic equations for this reaction.

C6c Alcohols

After revising this item you should:

- be able to compare the two main methods of ethanol production.

Alcohol formulae

The **alcohols** are a class of organic compounds that all have an OH group in the molecule. They have the general formula $C_nH_{2n+1}OH$.

The following diagram shows the best known alcohol – **ethanol**.

The next table shows the molecular and displayed formulae of the first five alcohols.

1	methanol CH_3OH	H–C–O–H with H above and H below the C
2	ethanol C_2H_5OH	H–C–C–O–H with H above and below each C
3	propanol C_3H_7OH	H–C–C–C–O–H with H above and below each C
4	butanol C_4H_9OH	H–C–C–C–C–O–H with H above and below each C
5	pentanol $C_5H_{11}OH$	H–C–C–C–C–C–O–H with H above and below each C

Fermentation

Ethanol can be made by fermenting glucose solution using **yeast**.

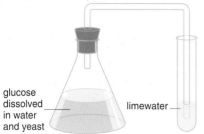

glucose dissolved in water and yeast   limewater

The reaction also produces carbon dioxide gas, which turns limewater milky.

$$glucose \longrightarrow ethanol + carbon\ dioxide$$
$$C_6H_{12}O_6 \longrightarrow 2C_2H_5OH + 2CO_2$$

You can make ethanol by **fermentation** like this:

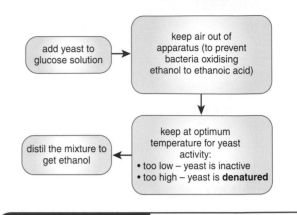

add yeast to glucose solution

keep air out of apparatus (to prevent bacteria oxidising ethanol to ethanoic acid)

keep at optimum temperature for yeast activity:
• too low – yeast is inactive
• too high – yeast is **denatured**

distil the mixture to get ethanol

How science works

A leading scientist comments 'Ethanol is a toxic chemical. If ethanol were discovered today, it would be banned from sale to the public.'

What are the benefits and drawbacks of making alcoholic drinks for sale to the public?

Industrial production of ethanol

Ethanol is an important industrial chemical. It is made for industrial use by passing ethene and steam over a heated phosphoric acid catalyst.

$$ethene + water \longrightarrow ethanol$$
$$C_2H_4 + H_2O \longrightarrow C_2H_5OH$$

Which is better?

Each method of making ethanol has advantages and disadvantages.

Method	Advantages	Disadvantages
fermentation	• simple to set up • requires a lower temperature • uses sustainable raw materials	• produces impure ethanol which requires distillation to purify it
produced from ethene	• produces pure ethanol	• complex to set up • requires a higher temperature and a catalyst • uses raw material usually obtained from crude oil

Making ethene

Ethene can be made by passing ethanol vapour over a heated aluminium oxide catalyst.

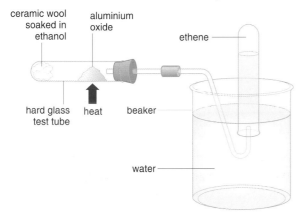

The reaction is known as **dehydration** because a molecule of water, H_2O, is removed from each molecule of ethanol.

$$\text{ethanol} \longrightarrow \text{ethene} + \text{water}$$
$$C_2H_5OH \longrightarrow C_2H_4 + H_2O$$

C6d Chemistry of sodium chloride (NaCl) & C6e Ozone layer depletion

Salt mines

There are vast deposits of salt beneath the ground in Cheshire. Large quantities of **rock salt**. (a mixture of salt, sand and rock) are mined in this area each year for use on icy roads.

Salt is also removed by **solution mining**.

1 Water is pumped underground to dissolve the salt.

2 The solution is then brought to the surface.

- This solution is called **brine**.

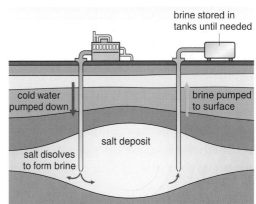

This mining activity can lead to **subsidence** of land on the surface above the mines.

Electrolysis of brine

We can produce important industrial raw materials by the electrolysis of brine, a concentrated solution of sodium chloride in water.

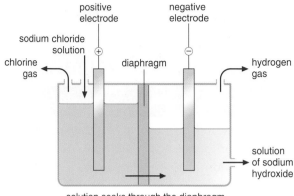

positive electrode

negative electrode

sodium chloride solution

chlorine gas

diaphragm

hydrogen gas

solution of sodium hydroxide

solution soaks through the diaphragm

Key features of this electrolysis are:

- inert carbon electrodes are used
- hydrogen is made at the negative electrode (cathode):

$$2H^+ + 2e^- \rightarrow H_2$$

- chlorine is made at the positive electrode (anode):

$$2Cl^- - 2e^- \rightarrow Cl_2$$

- the sodium and hydroxide ions that are not discharged make sodium hydroxide solution.

If a dilute solution of sodium chloride is electrolysed, the product at the anode is oxygen instead of chlorine.

- When there is a high concentration of chloride ions in the solution, chlorine is discharged.
- When there is a low concentration of chloride ions, hydroxide ions are discharged and this produces oxygen gas.

Electrolysis of molten sodium chloride

The electrolysis of molten sodium chloride also produces chlorine gas at the anode, but at the cathode molten sodium is discharged.

$$Na^+ + e^- \rightarrow Na$$

Household bleach

Household **bleach** is made by adding chlorine to sodium hydroxide solution. The active chemical in bleach is sodium chlorate.

chlorine +	sodium hydroxide	→	sodium chloride	+	sodium chlorate	+ water
Cl_2	+ NaOH	→	NaCl	+	NaOCl	+ H_2O

The rise and fall of CFCs

CFC is short for chlorofluorocarbon. An example is $CClF_3$.

- These compounds are chemically **inert**.
- This lack of reactivity led to their widespread use as refrigerants and aerosol propellants.

Towards the end of the last century scientists discovered that CFCs cause depletion of the **ozone layer**.

- Ozone absorbs **ultraviolet light** in the **stratosphere**.
- So a thinning of the ozone layer allows more harmful ultraviolet light to reach the surface of the Earth.

The discovery of ozone depletion by scientists led to the use of CFCs being banned in many countries. They have been replaced by alkanes and HFCs (hydrofluorocarbons) which do not damage the ozone layer.

How science works

Not all countries have banned the use of CFCs.

Why is it important to people in the United Kingdom that other countries do ban CFCs?

Why is it more difficult for some countries to ban the use of CFCs than others?

A chain reaction

A covalent bond can break unevenly to form ions (e.g. $Cl_2 \rightarrow Cl^+ + Cl^-$), which needs a lot of energy.

A covalent bond can break evenly to form **free radicals** (e.g. $Cl_2 \rightarrow 2 \bullet Cl$), which needs less energy.

Depletion of the ozone layer by CFCs results from a **chain reaction** involving free radicals.

The action of ultraviolet light on CFCs splits them to form chlorine atoms, which are chlorine free radicals.

$$CClF_3 \rightarrow \bullet CF_3 + \bullet Cl$$

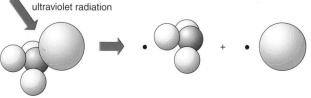

ultraviolet radiation

Chlorine free radicals react with ozone molecules, producing an oxygen molecule and another free radical.

$$\bullet Cl + O_3 \longrightarrow \bullet ClO + O_2$$

This free radical then takes part in more reactions which themselves produce free radicals – a chain reaction.

$$O_3 \longrightarrow O + O_2$$
$$\bullet ClO + O \longrightarrow \bullet Cl + O_2$$

The overall the reaction is:
$$2O_3 \longrightarrow 3O_2$$

Because this is a chain reaction, a small number of chlorine atoms (free radicals) will react with many ozone molecules.

CFCs are only removed slowly from the stratosphere. This means that even if their use is banned in all countries, they will continue to deplete the ozone layer for many years.

Test yourself

1 Why does an aerosol propellant need to be inert?

2 What is meant by the term free radical?

3 Why is it important for all countries to ban the use of CFCs as soon as possible?

4 Explain how sodium hydroxide is made during the electrolysis of brine.

5 Why is sodium produced during the electrolysis of molten sodium chloride but not during the electrolysis of brine?

C6f Hardness of water

After revising this item you should:

● understand what causes water hardness and how it can be removed.

What is hard water?

Dissolved carbon dioxide makes water slightly acidic.

● The acidic water reacts with calcium carbonate in rocks such as chalk, limestone and marble.

● A solution of calcium hydrogencarbonate is formed.

● This causes **temporary water hardness**.

calcium carbonate	+ water +	carbon dioxide	→	calcium hydrogen-carbonate
$CaCO_3$	+ H_2O +	CO_2	→	$Ca(HCO_3)_2$

Removing water hardness

You can boil water to destroy temporary hardness, making the water soft. Calcium hydrogencarbonate decomposes when heated.

$$Ca(HCO_3)_2 \longrightarrow CaCO_3 + H_2O + CO_2$$

Permanent water hardness is caused by dissolved calcium sulfate, which does not decompose when heated. So boiling does not remove permanent water hardness.

Both permanent and temporary hardness can be removed by:

● passing the water through an ion exchange column

● adding **washing soda** (sodium carbonate).

Sodium ions in an ion exchange column swap places with calcium ions in the hard water. Since sodium ions do not cause water hardness, the water becomes soft.

Water hardness may also be caused by compounds containing magnesium ions.

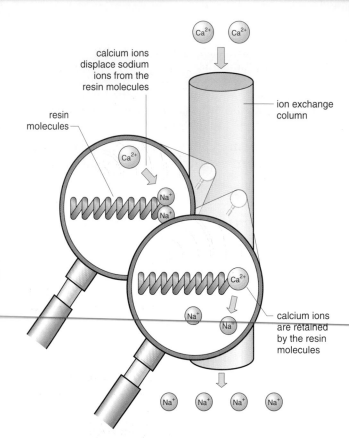

resin molecules

calcium ions displace sodium ions from the resin molecules

Ca²⁺ Ca²⁺

ion exchange column

Ca²⁺

Na⁺ Na⁺

Na⁺ Na⁺

Ca²⁺

calcium ions are retained by the resin molecules

Na⁺ Na⁺ Na⁺ Na⁺

Washing soda reacts with calcium ions in the water, forming calcium carbonate. This precipitates out of the water.

Measuring water hardness

Madhur measured the number of drops of soap solution needed to get a lather in different samples of water. The more drops that were needed, the greater the hardness of the water.

The results from her experiment are shown in the following table.

soap solution

lather

water sample being tested

Source of water sample	Drops of soap to get a lather
local tap water	36
boiled local tap water	24
distilled water	2

These results show that the local tap water contains both permanent and temporary hardness. When the water is boiled the temporary hardness is removed but the permanent hardness remains.

Distilled water does not contain any water hardness. It is tested as a control to be compared with the other results.

Exam tip

You may be asked how you would carry out an experiment to measure water hardness, or be given data from an experiment to interpret.

How science works

How could Madhur make sure that the results in her table are reliable?

Limescale removers

When water containing temporary hardness is boiled in a kettle, **limescale** forms on the kettle element. Limescale is calcium carbonate.

Limescale removers are acids. They react with the calcium carbonate, removing it from the kettle element. Weak acids, such as ethanoic acid, are used to prevent damage to the metal of the element. The reaction between ethanoic acid and calcium carbonate is shown at the bottom of the page.

Test yourself

1 How can you measure the amount of hardness in a sample of water?

2 Look at the table showing the results from Madhur's experiment (opposite). What do these results show about the hardness in her local tap water?

3 Explain how an ion exchange resin removes water hardness.

4 Why is temporary hardness a problem for kettles, but permanent hardness is not?

5 Jake looks at several acids to decide which is suitable for use as limescale remover.

citric acid   hydrochloric acid   sulfuric acid

State and explain which acid he should choose.

ethanoic acid + calcium carbonate → calcium ethanoate + carbon dioxide + water
$2CH_3COOH$ + $CaCO_3$ → $Ca(CH_3COO)_2$ + CO_2 + H_2O

C6g Natural fats and oils & C6h Analgesics

After revising these items you should:

● know details of the processes used to make margarine, soap and aspirin.

Saturated or unsaturated?

Animal and vegetable fats and oils are esters.

● Animal fats and oils are often saturated. This means that all of the carbon atoms are joined by single covalent bonds.

● Vegetable oils and fats are often unsaturated. This means that at least two carbon atoms are joined by a double bond.

● Unsaturated fats in our food are thought to be healthier than saturated fats. A diet rich in saturated fats may lead to heart disease.

Test for unsaturation

The following diagram shows how to find out if an oil or fat is saturated or unsaturated.

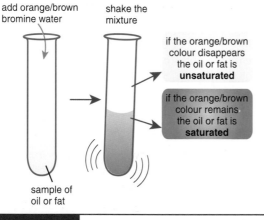

add orange/brown bromine water

shake the mixture

if the orange/brown colour disappears the oil or fat is **unsaturated**

if the orange/brown colour remains the oil or fat is **saturated**

sample of oil or fat

Exam tip

To get full marks for describing the 'bromine test', always state the colour before and after the test, and give details of both the positive and negative results.

Making margarine

Margarine is made by adding hydrogen to unsaturated oils in the presence of a catalyst. This makes the oil more saturated, turning it from a liquid into a soft solid.

Emulsions

Vegetable oil and water are **immiscible** liquids. They do not mix. If you shake them and leave them to stand, the two liquids separate out.

But if you add a stabiliser they can be made to mix. They form an emulsion.

● With water in excess an oil-in-water emulsion is made, with small droplets of oil spread through the water.

● With oil in excess a water-in-oil emulsion is formed, with small droplets of water spread through the oil.

Making soap

The esters in natural fats and oils can be split up by heating them with sodium hydroxide. This process is called **saponification**, and makes soap and **glycerol**.

fat + sodium hydroxide $\longrightarrow$ soap + glycerol

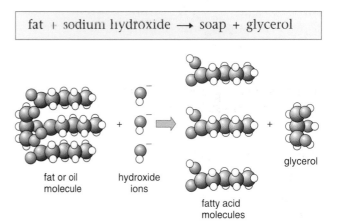

fat or oil molecule

hydroxide ions

fatty acid molecules

glycerol

The reaction is called a **hydrolysis**, because water is added to the oil or fat in the reaction.

Aspirin

A drug is an externally administered substance that modifies or affects chemical reactions in the body. **Aspirin** is an **analgesic** – a drug that relieves pain.

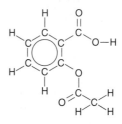

Two other commonly used analgesics are **paracetamol** and **ibuprofen**.

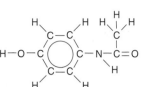

Paracetamol

Like all other drugs, these analgesics must be made from chemicals that are very pure.

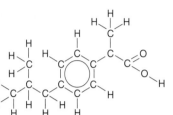

Ibuprofen

Soluble aspirin

Aspirin can cause stomach ulcers. This side effect can be avoided by using **soluble aspirin**. Soluble aspirin is created by reacting non-soluble aspirin with sodium hydroxide.

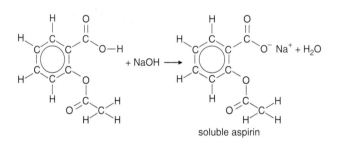

soluble aspirin

Soluble aspirin has a negative charge. This is attracted towards the small positive charges on water molecules, enabling it to dissolve in water. Non-soluble aspirin has no charge.

Soluble aspirin works faster as it dissolves very rapidly and enters the bloodstream more quickly than non-soluble aspirin.

Aspirin has other side effects. It reduces the tendency of the blood to clot. It can lead to internal bleeding.

Both aspirin and paracetamol are toxic, leading to a danger of death through overdose.

Manufacture of aspirin

Aspirin is made from **salicylic acid** and ethanoic anhydride, kept at 90°C for 20 hours. When the mixture is then cooled, aspirin crystallises out.

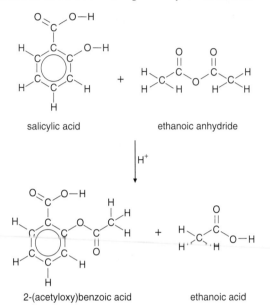

salicylic acid   ethanoic anhydride

2-(acetyloxy)benzoic acid   ethanoic acid

How science works

Before aspirin was manufactured some people used willow bark to relieve pain.

Willow bark contains salicylic acid, which forms a solution of about pH 3 and causes severe irritation of the mouth and stomach.

How have scientists improved on the use of willow bark as an analgesic?

Test yourself

1 What is the difference between a fat and oil?

2 How can soap be made from olive oil?

3 The molecular formula of aspirin is $C_9H_8O_4$. What is the molecular formula of ibuprofen?

4 Use ideas about their displayed formulae to explain why soluble aspirin dissolves in water but non-soluble aspirin does not.

5 Why is soluble aspirin a better analgesic than non-soluble aspirin?

Exam-style questions

1 Polystyrene is an addition polymer.

(a) Explain what is meant by the term **addition polymer**.

....

....[2]

(b) The diagram shows part of the displayed formula of polystyrene.

$$
\begin{array}{cccccccccccc}
 & H & & C_6H_5 & & H & & C_6H_5 & & H & & C_6H_5 \\
 & | & & | & & | & & | & & | & & | \\
- & C & - & C & - & C & - & C & - & C & - & C & - \\
 & | & & | & & | & & | & & | & & | \\
 & H & & H & & H & & H & & H & & H
\end{array}
$$

Draw the displayed formula of the monomer from which polystyrene is made.

[2]

(c) Polystyrene is used in the packing of electrical goods to prevent damage in transit. What property of polystyrene makes it a good choice for this use?

.. ..[1]

(d) Polystyrene has a fairly low melting point. Some other polymers have much higher melting points. Explain this difference. Use ideas about forces between polymer molecules.

....

....

....[3]

2 Along the western coast of South America an oceanic plate is colliding with and sliding beneath a continental plate.

(a) **(i)** What name is given to this process?

....[2]

(ii) What does this process show about the density of these plates?

....[1]

(iii) Explain what causes tectonic plates to move. A diagram may help you.

....

....[2]

(b) The western coast of South America is an area of volcanic activity. Lava released from volcanoes forms igneous rocks.

(i) Some igneous rocks have large crystals whilst others have small crystals.

Explain this difference.

....

....[2]

(ii) Geologists study volcanoes. Who may benefit from this study? Explain why.

....

....[2]

3 **(a)** Sodium is a metal in Group 1 and iron is a transition element.

State **one** property of a compound of a transition element that is not shown by a Group 1 metal compound.

....[1]

(b) Sodium compounds can be identified using a flame test. Describe how to carry out a flame test.

....

....

....[3]

(c) The table below shows some properties of some Group 1 metals.

Element	Boiling point (°C)	Reaction with oxygen
sodium	883	steadily
potassium	760	rapidly
rubidium	698	
caesium		explosively

(i) Predict the boiling point of caesium.

....[1]

(ii) Predict how rubidium will react with oxygen.

....[1]

(d) Iron has a high melting point. Use ideas about the bonding in iron to explain why this is.

....

....

....[3]

(e) Iron(II) carbonate, $FeCO_3$, decomposes when heated. Write a balanced symbol equation for this reaction.

....[1]

4 **(a)** Diamond and graphite are forms of carbon. What name is given to different forms of the same element?

....[1]

(b) What property of graphite makes it useful as a lubricant?

....[1]

(c) Explain why graphite conducts electricity.

....[1]

(d) Nanotubes are also a form of carbon. Nanotubes can be used in catalysis.

Explain how and why nanotubes are used in catalysis.

....
....[2]

(e) In a blast furnace, carbon is heated with iron(III) oxide to form iron and carbon monoxide.

$Fe_2O_3 + 3CO \longrightarrow 2Fe + 3CO_2$

Calculate the mass of iron formed when 320 tonnes of iron(III) oxide react completely. (O = 16, Fe = 56)

....
....
....
....
....[3]

(f) Most dry-cleaning fluids are carbon-based organic molecules. Explain in terms of intermolecular forces how dry-cleaning fluids remove the greasy dirt from clothes.

....
....
....[2]

5 Compound A is a weak acid.

(a) Explain the difference between a strong acid and a weak acid.

....
....[2]

(b) Compound A has the following percentage composition: carbon 40%, hydrogen 6.7%, oxygen 53.3%.

Calculate the empirical formula of compound A.
(C = 12; H = 1; O = 16)

....
....
....[3]

(c) Propanoic acid is a weak acid. When reacted with methanol it forms an ester.

propanoic   +   methanol $\rightleftharpoons$ methyl   +   water
acid   propanoate

$CH_3CH_2CO_2H + CH_3OH \rightleftharpoons CH_3CH_2CO_2CH_3 + H_2O$

(i) This is an equilibrium reaction. State **two** characteristics of an equilibrium reaction.

....
....[2]

(ii) How could you increase the yield of the ester, methyl propanoate?

....[1]

(iii) Calculate the mass of 0.5 moles of propanoic acid.
(C = 12; H = 1; O = 16)

[3]

(d) A solution of propanoic acid, pH 4, is titrated with a $0.1\,mol/dm^3$ solution of sodium hydroxide, pH 13. Sketch a pH titration curve to show how the pH changes as the sodium hydroxide solution is added to the solution of propanoic acid.

[4]

6 Amy investigates the rusting of iron. She places iron nails with different methods of rust protection in water and observes them for a few hours. Her results are shown in the table.

Iron nail	Result
unprotected	iron rusts slowly
covered with tin	no rust
covered with tin and scratched	iron rusts quickly
attached to a piece of magnesium	no rust

(a) Why does Amy set up the unprotected iron nail as part of her experiment?

....[1]

(b) **(i)** Explain why the nail covered with tin does not rust.

....[1]

(ii) Explain why the nail covered with tin and scratched rusts quickly.

....
....[2]

(c) To understand what happened to the nail attached to a piece of magnesium, Amy carries out another experiment.

She adds some magnesium powder to iron(II) sulfate solution. The green colour of the iron(II) sulfate solution disappears.

Amy concludes that the magnesium has displaced iron from the iron(II) sulfate solution.

(i) Write an equation for this displacement.

....
....[2]

(ii) In this displacement what has been oxidised? Explain your answer.

....
....[2]

(iii) Explain why the iron nail attached to a piece of magnesium did not rust. Use ideas from the displacement reaction.

....
....[2]

Answers to exam-style questions

1 (a) Large molecules made by adding together small molecules; With no other product [2]

(b) A diagram showing two carbon atoms joined by a double bond; Three hydrogen atoms and one C_6H_5 group joined to the carbon atoms [2]

(c) Hard / strong [1]

(d) Melting point depends on the forces of attraction between molecules / chains; Polystyrene has weak forces; Other polymers have stronger crosslinking [3]

2 (a) (i) Subduction [1]

(ii) Oceanic plates are denser than continental plates [1]

(iii) Convection currents; In the magma [2]

(b) (i) Slow cooling below ground forms large crystals; Rapid cooling above ground forms small crystals [2]

(ii) People living near active volcanoes; They may get early warning of an eruption [2]

3 (a) Transition element compounds are coloured / are catalysts [1]

(b) Moisten a nichrome / platinum wire; Dip the wire into the solid compound; Put the compound on the wire at the edge of a blue Bunsen flame [3]

(c) (i) Values between 620°C and 680°C (actual value is 669°C) [1]

(ii) Very rapidly / indication of more rapidly than potassium but less rapidly than caesium [1]

(d) Metallic bonding due to metal cations / positive ions in sea of electrons / delocalised electrons; Strong forces of attraction between the cations

and electrons; Takes a lot of energy to break these strong forces [3]

(e) $FeCO_3 \longrightarrow FeO + CO_2$ [1]

4 (a) Allotrope(s) [1]

(b) Slippery(ness) [1]

(c) Delocalised electrons can move (not electrons can move) [1]

(d) Small groups of catalyst atoms attached to outside of nanotubes; Provide a large surface area for catalysis [2]

(e) RMM of Fe_2O_3 = (56 × 2) + (16 × 3) = 160; 160 tonnes of Fe_2O_3 will give 56 × 2 = 112 tonnes of Fe; 320 tonnes of Fe_2O_3 gives 224 tonnes of Fe (apply transferred error) [3]

(f) Intermolecular forces of attraction between grease molecules and dry-cleaning fluid molecules; Allows grease molecules to dissolve in dry-cleaning fluid [2]

5 (a) Strong acid completely ionised (in solution in water); Weak acid only partially ionised (in solution in water) / has molecules as well as ions (when in solution) / produces an equilibrium mixture of molecules and ions [2]

(b) Divide by atomic masses: C = 40/12 = 3.33, H = 6.7/1 = 6.7, O = 53.3/16 = 3.33; Divide by smallest: C = 3.33/3.33, H = 6.7/3.33, O = 3.33/3.33; Ratio: C = 1, H = 2, O = 1 so empirical formula is CH_2O (allow transferred error from first to second step) [3]

(c) (i) Any **two** from: Rate of forward reaction = rate of back reaction / Concentrations at equilibrium do not change / Can only occur in a closed system [2]

(ii) Any **one** from: Remove water; Add more reactants / propanoic acid / methanol (not effects of pressure / temperature) [1]

(iii) Molar mass of propanoic acid = (3 × 12) + (2 × 16) + (6 × 1) = 74 (g); mass = moles × molar mass / mass = 0.5 × 74; 37 g (unit required) [3]

(d) Labelled axes: 'pH' on vertical axis, 'Volume of sodium hydroxide' on horizontal axis; pH starts at '4' and ends at '12' / '13' (allow pH ends at 11); pH does not change significantly / changes very gradually when acid first added and at the end; Central part of curve shows very rapid change in pH (vertical or near-vertical line) [4]

6 (a) As a control / for comparison [1]

(b) (i) Tin prevents water and oxygen from coming into contact with the iron [1]

(ii) Water and oxygen can get to the iron in the scratch / the tin no longer stops water and oxygen coming into contact with the iron; Tin is less reactive than iron so the iron rusts more quickly instead of the tin corroding [2]

(c) (i) $Mg + FeSO_4 \longrightarrow Fe + MgSO_4$ (one mark for each side of the equation) [2]

(ii) Magnesium; Because it has lost electrons to make ions [2]

(iii) Magnesium displaces iron so it must be more reactive than iron; Magnesium protects iron by sacrificial corrosion / by corroding instead of iron [2]

Index of key words